The Chinese Five Word Song

written by
Master Li Tung

original translation and commentary by
Master John Chung Li

Hwa-Yu T'ai-Chi Health and Well-Being

Grace Martial Arts Fellowship

For information for first time authors, address Fifth Estate Publishers, Post Office Box 116, Blountsville, AL 35031 205-625-5733.

First Edition

Edited by Mark McGee
Designed by Lori Gibbs

Printed on acid-free paper

Library of Congress Control Number 2004101463

ISBN 0-9746336-0-7

Fifth Estate 02/04

Introduction

Tradition has it that the principles of Hwa-Yu T'ai-Chi Ch'uan were created by Master Chen Hsi-I (pronounced Chin-Hee). Master Hsi-I lived in the Hwa Shan mountain range in Shansi during the early part of the Sung Dynasty (960-1279 AD). Hwa-Yu T'ai-Chi Ch'uan is an ancient Chinese temple-style meditation in movement; an internal martial art health care science. Hwa-Yu T'ai-Chi Ch'uan incorporates the best principles of all three internal martial arts styles (T'ai Chi Ch'uan, Pa Kua Chang, Hsing I Ch'uan) and was first known by the name Liu Ho Pa Fa (Lop Hop Pak Fat). It translates as "Six Combinations Eight Methods." The name was later changed to "Swimming Box." It has also been known as "Twelve Movements of Exercise Before Birth," "Idea Six Combination Boxing," and "Idea Spiritual Boxing."

Master Hsi-I was drawn to Hwa Yu Mountain -- Hwa Yu means Beautiful Place Within -- to find seclusion. During his life there he was recognized with having created the T'ai-Chi Ruler and many other Chi Kung exercises still practiced today. The Long Form Master Hsi-I created comprises hundreds of sequenced, rounded, gracefully balanced movement patterns. Through diligent practice of the Form, grounded solidly in the principles of the Six Combinations Eight Methods, every student has the potential to attain immense internal energy.

The benefits of Hwa-Yu T'ai-Chi Ch'uan are amazing. The martial exercise promotes strength and increases bone density and suppleness in the joints and limbs through twisting, bending and stretching movements that also free limbs from harmful adhesions. The daily exercise program will serve to counter negative, cumulative daily stress, while lowering blood pressure, increasing circulation, stamina and re-energizing a person both mentally and physically.

Master Li Tung Fung was the senior student of Master Chen Hsi-I. Master Hsi-I is credited with creating the famous Liu Ho Pa Fa (Lop Hop Pak Fat) Martial Art system and passing the lineage to Master Fung at the beginning of China's Sung Dynasty (960 - 1279 AD).

After studying with Hsi-I, Master Fung took refuge in Yun Mountain and authored the famous <u>Chinese Five Word Song</u> (translated for this book). It is the only extant treatise explaining the principles of the original <u>Lop Hop Pak Fat</u>.

Chinese poetry has been passed from generation to generation for thousands of years. Classic poetry was very popular by the end of the Tang Dynasty (618-907 A.D.). Many ancient poems had five syllables per line. Many poems from the Tang Dynasty were made up of five words per line, as in <u>The Chinese Five Word Song</u>, also translated as <u>The Chinese Five Character Song</u>. You will find five hand-written Chinese characters above every verse in the Appendix of this document. Poetry of the Sung Dynasty was often based on tunes of popular songs of the day. Martial arts masters have long used poetry and music to help students remember important aspects of exercises and the order of health and self defense forms.

<u>The Chinese Five Word Song</u> has been passed from master to student for centuries. Some of the previous Masters of <u>Lop Hop Pak Fat</u> include Kwan Kit, Lan Wan Sing, Wong Tak Wai, Ta Yai Chin, Yeung King Kun, Chen Kong Ta, Wu Yiek Tai, Chan Yik-Yan, Lo Chi-wan and John Chung Li. Master Li said his main objective for moving from China to the United States in the late 1960's was to impart the numerous health care benefits of the Art to the American people. Master Li showed his students the many impressive martial art applications of Hwa-Yu T'ai-Chi Ch'uan, but always emphasized correct kinetic posturing and movement principles to enhance the many health care benefits of the exercise.

One of Master John Chung Li's senior instructors, Robert Xavier, provided me with three copies of Master Li's translation of Li Tung Fung's <u>Chinese Five Word Song</u>. Master Li also added commentary to each of the 134 verses of the Song with the assistance of Mr. Terry Thompson. Additional commentary provided in this text came from audio tapes of Master Li's Boston lectures during the 1970's.

I want to extend my appreciation to Master Xavier for allowing me to transcribe the original writings and audio tapes of Master John Chung Li and to include photographs of Master Li demonstrating the Long Form of Hwa-Yu T'ai-Chi Ch'uan. We are pleased the time has arrived to publish this amazing document, written by Li Tung Fung 1,000 years ago, with Master John Chung Li's commentary. Our hope is The Chinese Five Word Song will benefit you in all aspects of your life; including health and self defense.

Mark McGee, Editor
February 2004

Five Word Song Forward
By Robert F. Xavier, DD, Ph.D.

In 1975 I was awarded certification as a Senior Instructor of the prestigious martial art healthcare science by Master Li of the Hwa-Yu T'ai-Chi Health Institute. As I continued my studies, Master Li shared with his students <u>The Chinese Five Word Song</u> treatise explaining the principles and origin of Hwa-Yu T'ai-Chi Ch'uan. The verses of the original manuscript were written with five Chinese characters in rhyme and poetry, much like the Psalms of the Bible.

The serious T'ai-Chi practitioner will discover unparalleled ancient legendary secrets for health and well-being. Your mind will become dramatically revitalized, and many long-kept secret healthcare principles and methods will be revealed by its daily reading.

A Hwa-Yu T'ai-Chi choreographed movement vocabulary can be compared to the car one drives. The car needs a driver, the practitioner. <u>The Chinese Five Word Song</u> is the manual that provides the mind intent which guides and assists the driver in the operation of his/her car. <u>The Chinese Five Word Song</u> manual script, as translated by Grand Master John Chung Li, is universally accepted by historians as an excellent authentic literary work. It provides guided discovery that makes a major contribution to help serious martial arts and T'ai-Chi practitioners to reach **ultimate balance in exercise and life**.

The three major components required to be able to apply effectively the 134 verses of <u>The Chinese Five Word Song</u> to one's life and martial arts practice are: <u>wisdom</u>, <u>knowledge</u> and <u>understanding</u>. Through your guided discovery, you will embrace <u>knowledge</u> of the kinetic laws of physics that are universally cohesive with spherical movement. What's more, the meditations of <u>The Chinese Five Word Song</u> will provide you with much more than <u>knowledge</u> and <u>wisdom</u>. You will be enlightened with the many practical applications of the multitude of hidden treasures in this book for your life relationships as well as your T'ai-Chi exercise.

Information Verses Life Formation

Information alone seldom facilitates positive, lasting physical or emotional change. Through combined wisdom and knowledge with a practical understanding, life formation is realized. Applying The Chinese Five Word Song insights and mind intent with your T'ai-Chi practice will immensely advance harmony of body, mind and spirit. It will internalize the natural state of awareness process as you become perfectly natural, completely practical and intensely spiritual. Grand Master John Chung Li understood, lived and experienced more than **ultimate, extreme T'ai-Chi balance**. His movement flowed from a divine essence of grace-centered worship. He practiced the presence of God within each movement. He applied real life formation and inner peace from the one true God, Creator and Savior, the Lord Jesus Christ. He received God's gift of unconditional love, acceptance and forgiveness that casts away excessive stress and worries. This was Mr. Li's one true secret to wholeness. My friend and teacher performed perfect whole body harmony of movement above his peers because he had discovered the true secret of inner strength. "Before honor is humility." Enjoy your journey inwardly, upwardly and outwardly.

Affectionately His Student & Your Friend,

Mr. Bob

The Chinese Five Word Song

By

Master Li Tung Fung

1) Empty the Mind.

2) If one thinks there is a method, that thought is in vain.

3) By making the mind void of thoughts, one can gain a natural meditative state.

4) With a calm mind, one is free from hesitation.

5) A quiet mind opens the pathway to harmony within and without.

6) Fill the sky and the earth within as well as without.

7) This is like the Buddhist's idea conveyed by the circle.

8) The Taoists say it is not one's will, but the will of nature.

9) At first while doing the exercise, one reveals each feature of the movement, but with practice the features flow into one.

10) This fluidness of movement cannot be anticipated; through practice it comes naturally.

11/12) If one wishes to learn this internal exercise, then one must first learn the eight methods.

13) This exercise maintains one's broadminded spirit.

14) The entire body is elastic (spring-like).

15) The beginning of the internal force can be recognized by the opponent.

16) When the exercise is mastered, one's feature and intent are unrecognizable.

17) Movement to and fro is not revealed.

18) Relaxing and flexing of movement are self-determined.

19) One must meet attack by being calm.

20) The body should be straight in stance.

21) The opponent sees no resistance in your stance, but this is false for you are concealed.

22) If one does not practice regularly, then do not face the enemy.

23) When in motion one is still rooted.

24) Do not overextend yourself to the opponent.

25) Judge the chance and take the opportunity.

26) One strikes with internal force before the opponent advances with strength.

27) When the opponent is hard, then one is soft.

28) Although the opponent is busy, one stays calm awaiting him.

29) He is busy attacking you; you should calmly wait.

30) To attack or protect is according to one's decision.

31) Take the first opportunity and be quicker than the opponent.

32) Always concentrate on the situation.

33) Conceal one's force like the bow: round and ready to spring.

34) Attack as the arrow - quick and straight.

35) One should thoroughly understand the principle of yin-yang.

36) Both the yin and yang flow in and out, hard and soft, and are of mutual use.

37) Breathing is regular from the bottom of the abdomen to the heart.

38) This cyclic up and down breathing smooths the Chi.

39) Be calm as the resting Buddhist.

40) Move like a dragon rising from hibernation.

41) This calmness appears empty but there is something within.

42/43) The internal force which is wonderfully rewarding can be suddenly concealed, and suddenly expressed.

44) All breathing shall be natural.

45) Yield to heavy attack.

46) Every action is self-initiated.

47) Distribution of weight between one leg and the other is clearly distinguished.

48) The body is of both yin and yang, both empty and solid.

49) By emptying oneself, the opponent's force is led to a void.

50) If the enemy retreats, stick with quick advance.

51) The legs should be curved like a bow.

52) Advancing and retreating use force derived from the kidney.

53) The arms and back should be round as if hugging.

54) Circulate your Chi from the inside to the outside.

55/56) Stop trivial thoughts and concentrate on your movement, as if facing a difficult enemy.

57) Your eyes move about like lightning.

58) Your spirit watches in all four directions (front, back, left, right).

59) Your footing should be 40% to the front and 60% to the rear.

60) The hands are 30% to the front and 70% to the rear.

61) The feature of the movement is like swimming in the water.

62/63) Movement is light, like a fairy in the clouds.

64) The idea is very great, but there is nothing; it is like a great void.

65) The idea of the movement is like a fierce tiger.

66) The calmness of Chi is very gentle.

67) Once the enemy is on the offensive, the enemy is defeated.

68) The inner strength controls the Five Terminals and the Nine Joints.

69) If one wants to learn, then one must practice frequently.

70) In this way studying and practice of the exercise enables a deeper progress to be made. From the door to the hall to the chamber with one's master.

71) When the exercise is mastered, one's inner force can be concealed or expressed at will.

72) Focus the Spirit to discover the Truth.

73) This harmonious exercise combines all the movement.

74) The quiet and emptiness of this exercise separates one from worldly things.

75/76) Remember all progress towards the truth of this exercise is very delicate.

77) The idea of movement is to seem not to move - achieving fluidness.

78) One's calmness combines with the idea.

79) Cease all thoughts, and your Chi will become calm naturally.

80) Quietly maintain the "great emptiness."

81) One's basic foundation is built through this exercise.

82) In this exercise, all valuable points are concealed.

83) It is hard to learn: no, it is not.

84) It looks easy at first, but it is not easy.

85) If one's mind is made up to learn, then there will be success.

86) In this world there is nothing of real difficulty.

87) To learn, one must be sincere and determined.

88) To learn correctly depends on long frequent practice and on your wisdom.

89) This exercise was invented by Ch'en Hsi-I of Hwa Yu.

90) The student of Hwa Yu should practice every day. This is most important.

91) There must be concentration of spirit and idea (will).

92) All the joints of the body move together.

93) When contact is made, the inner force comes forth at once.

94) This gives no opportunity for the opponent to escape.

95) The opponent thinks you are relaxed, but you are not relaxed (inner force).

96) The opponent thinks you are tense, but there is no strength.

97) All the movement is balanced in a circular fashion.

98) The Chi should be controlled to flow in and out as in a spiraling circle.

99) Do not be afraid of the opponent.

100) Open and close oneself and be able to yield and stick.

101) Watch for the enemy's weak point...

102) ...and once discovered attack without delay.

103) The wrist, elbow, shoulder, hip and knee are all combined.

104) Movement of legs and hands all work together.

105) All the joints work in combination with the Geng (inner force).

106) If this is achieved, there is no chance for the enemy to attack.

107) One's breathing is like the falling of fine cotton.

108) Therefore, your breathing can be up or down, slow or fast.

109) When the method is mastered, any attack can be met.

110) Strive for knowledge of the method, but also the wisdom (craft) of its usage.

111) Method and wisdom are joined into one.

112) Both concepts are very important; there cannot be one without the other.

113) Both hands raise up lightly.

114) Bend and stretch fluidly.

115) All turning and bending is curved.

116) The Form is like a swimming dragon in play.

117) Therefore, all sides move up or down, left or right.

118) This type of exercise follows the way of yin and yang.

119) The idea is formed and the Chi follows.

120) The inner force is concealed within the joints.

121) Relax your muscles and activate your blood vessels.

122) This is good for one's health.

123) When inhaling, the Chi rises.

124) When exhaling, the Chi sinks to the tan t'ien.

125) As soon as the Chi rises, it is swallowed and sinks down.

126) (In the flow of Chi) fire from below and water from above meet harmoniously.

127) Carefully study this inside and outside Kung Fu.

128) The mind (heart) should be empty; the abdomen should be solid.

129) At the moment of opportunity, attack at once.

130) The beginning and end of hardness and softness are inseparable.

131) The outside and inside force are mutually interchangeable.

132) Activity and inactivity follow one's will.

133/134) Those who set out to learn the exercise, do not misjudge the value of The Five Word Song.   *Also translated as The Five Character Song*

Hwa Yu Mountain

China

Birthplace of Hwa-Yu T'ai-Chi Ch'uan

(Beautiful Place Within Grand Ultimate Fist)

The Chinese Five Word Song

translation and commentary by

Master John Chung Li

1) Empty the Mind.

When we begin to practice this exercise, we should put all thoughts away from our mind. When our mind is empty (free from internal dialogue), we can concentrate on our movements and thus make progress. That's very important to empty your mind. Empty. Empty should calm your mind. Empty your mind. Empty your mind, then we can return to the Truth. You are so calm in your mind, you can find out the reason why. You can find the Truth by meditation.

2) If one thinks there is a method, that thought is in vain.

This means that if you have a preconceived idea about the art of Hwa Yu (or anything), that thought could distort the reality by trying to conform the reality to the idea of the mind. Why waste time with what you think when the reality is an unknown.

If we are without thought of method, there is more fluidity to our movement. Keep nothing in your mind while you practice, and concentrate on the coordination of your movement.

3) By making the mind void of thoughts, one can gain a natural meditative state.

With a quiet mind, meditate on all your movements, and enjoy your study.

All our movement should be moved in natural and go to the natural state. The natural state -- empty your mind.

If you gain the natural state, you are satisfied. You're happy and you enjoy internal and external as well. The natural state means harmony with the universe. Inside you have the world. Outside you have the world and the two worlds are harmonious.

When you move you relax your head; float in the air. You seem like you're floating in the air. These are harmonies with the universe. In this there is a bright circle in your mind. You're happy. You're bright. Wherever you go this circle reveals in the glow around the Buddhists head and glows around in the Taoist's heart. They are content, happy and enjoy living with what they have; desire nothing more. You gain this natural state. You're very happy, enjoy it. Therefore, inside you are happy. Outside, whatever you are, you're still happy.

In our exercise all movements are natural, floating continually to one; without beginning, without stopping, without any thought of self defense. You are floating yourself up and down. Enjoy. When you enjoy yourself, you are very happy.

This movement makes you to reach the highest point in your exercise: very happy. Enjoy yourselves, and this with your heart resting. You are resting. You are not in a hurry. You are resting, and light, not heavy. Very light. The longer you practice, the more you like it. That's true!

There is no way of anticipating how long you reach this natural state, but practice frequently - good to the body. If you say, Mr. Li, who can get the natural state, I can't tell you. Somebody can get ready quick and somebody can take a long time. Depends on your understanding.

In the Bible they talk about the natural state of Christians. In Philippians Chapter One verse 21: "To me to live is Christ." Christ means Natural. He's the Word of God. Everything come natural. A believer seeks the Truth, finds the Truth and lives in the Truth and the Truth lives in him and He's the Life. In this world you may be happy as in finite world. You can be happy because Christ lives in you. Christ is Truth. The Truth in you, or the God in you, this is the Natural State. Christians are the children of God. If Christ lives in you, you are the children of God. They have a Father in Heaven and no worry. No worry is the natural state of Christians. The Christian mind they no worry. God is their Father. The Father looks after him. No worry. No worry.

The Five Word Song will help us get the natural state to enjoy our life. We move the natural state and we're happy and peaceful in practicing our Internal exercise: Hwa-Yu T'ai-Chi Ch'uan. So, we must move to the natural state and you enjoy your circle always. Wherever you go you should do.

4) With a calm mind, one is free from hesitation.

The body moves fastest from a calm, relaxed posture or stance. If your mind is not calm, if it is busy with thoughts, your Chi will not flow because Chi will only flow through relaxation and calmness. If you are not moving with or from Chi, your movement is not natural and will be forced. It will not be as smooth and fluid as it should be. In the natural state you can enjoy your inside and outside movements. There are no interruptions and there are no questions to your soft, peaceful movements.

5) A quiet mind opens the pathway to harmony within and without.

Harmony can come to all the tiny organisms of your body. Your awareness of this new harmony, which is quickly felt throughout the body, will encourage you to practice every day.

6) Fill the sky and the earth within as well as without.

During your practice time you create a world which is like paradise, even while the world around you remains troubled. Your mind and heart will fill the sky and the earth.

7) This is like the Buddhist's idea conveyed by the circle.

When you make your own peaceful world, you move within a flowing circle.

8) The Taoists say it is not one's will, but the will of nature.

The Tao means the will of nature which is unknown. There is a story of Chen Hsi-I, who besides being the inventor of Hwa Yu, was an expert in the I-Ching, a scholar, a warrior and a Taoist philosopher. When he was asked to help the emperor (Chin Hon Yun) to consolidate his holdings, Chen Hsi-I informed the emperor that he needed no help because it was the emperor's destiny to be ruler. They decided to settle that matter at a chess game. If the emperor won, then Chen Hsi-I was bound by oath to aid him. The emperor, however, was preoccupied with troubles of the state, and was unable to defeat

14

Chen Hsi-I. So, in recompense, the Hwa Shan mountains were given to Chen Hsi-I. While hermitaging in the mountain range, he developed the Hwa Yu exercise. For this invention, he is also known as the sleeping fairy.

9) At first while doing the exercise, one reveals each feature of the movement, but with practice the features flow into one.

When you first begin to practice the exercise, each movement appears to be separate from the previous one. Since there are many ideas within each movement, you must learn the Form so well that in the later stage all the movements may flow smoothly and continuously into one.

10) This fluidity of movement cannot be anticipated; through practice it comes naturally.

Without beginning, without stopping, without any thought of self-defense one will obtain the highest state. When your movement is fluid, the mind is light and restful. It may take a long time to reach this natural state. So, practice frequently and be good to your body.

11/12) If one wishes to learn this internal exercise, then one must first learn the eight methods.

With the eight methods we can move from the simple to the advanced state. What are the Eight Methods?

(1) CHI   The Chi works internally as an energy source which circulates your blood. Chi emanates from an area called the <u>Tan T'ien</u> (the Sea of Chi), located about one and one-half inches below the navel. The <u>Tan T'ien</u> is the source of energy from which all movement springs, and lies dormant within everybody until it is activated by constant practice in the exercise. Since Spirit guides all our movement, Spirit assists the movement of our Chi, and Chi without Spirit is dull. The Spirit comes through the eye. Chi without Spirit is dull. The Spirit is shown in the eyes and in all movement.

Spirit is full attention. The Spirit means your whole attention, movement and meditation and Chi together, and Geng as well. It helps the movement of Chi. In the Advanced State we combine the Spirit and Chi and direct it with our mind. The Spirit and Chi all come together and the movements are pleasurable. Show the Spirit in your eyes and in all your movements. Have the Spirit of the dragon, and you will move like the dragon.

The Spirit expresses the whole movement up and down, left and right. If we have Spirit of a dragon, we will move like a dragon. The Spirit comes from inside your mind. You have something inside your mind. I wish to move as a dragon, up and down, and the Chi and the Spirit and you wake up as a dragon. We will move like a dragon.

(2) BONE   The internal force (Geng strength) is concealed within the bones and joints. The nature of this internal force is to come forth suddenly when needed, and then to subside. The internal work is more forceful if we push from the hind leg which is rooted to the ground. If in the beginning we practice the proper way to root ourselves, then in the advanced state, our internal work will be more forceful. That's why the first lesson I talk to you is about an important thing: footing. You must stand firmly. Root the ground first, otherwise no use. So, when you root to the ground, and your strength is in your hind leg and heel. In the beginning, we must practice all the time to be rooted.

If you practice, you have it. If you don't practice, you have no Chi, no Geng. It cannot be explained what is internal force. However, its nature comes suddenly when needed and then it subsides.

In the natural state, our natural work is more forceful. If you do more, you go to the Advanced State. If you at that time do the inside work, you're more forceful. Just a touch by your body and people fall. So, when you meet the enemy you don't worry how to touch.

(3) FEATURE From the time we learn our first movement, as well as the acquisition of each successive movement, we must do the Form properly; each movement should be clearly distinguished from the other. In the advanced state the movements in the Form are smoothed into a circle so that there is fluid and continuous movement.

In the Advanced State the Form is smoothed into a circle by fluid and continual movement. In this higher state you should continue without stopping - evenly, smoothly, continuously. Also in the Advanced State the Form is adaptable to many uses. In Hwa-Yu Pushing Hands we will learn not to anticipate our opponent's movement. We must always be ready for change. In Push Hands you don't know what kind of movement is going against you. If you practice well in the Advanced State, you know how to move. The Form is not the real exercise. Formless is the Truth. That means no feature; they didn't tell you how to do it. That's Truth. Therefore, we practice daily to move to the Advanced State. So, we practice very often and your practice is endless. The more you practice, the more you understand.

(4) FOLLOW In pushing hands we use stick-and-follow. Without anticipating your opponent's move, you lightly stick with his every movement, at once yielding to oncoming force, while leaving him no chance to advance. In this manner we can thoroughly understand our opponent's intentions - how he wishes to attack. Only he is never certain of where you are because your touch is so light.

Because we stick to the enemy, my hand touches the enemy and knows what he wishes because you have learned by feeling. This is the way to practice that exercise.

(5) RISE   One's head is held as if it were suspended from above, yet relaxed. Remember, the principles of T'ai Chi are the same as those which guide the I-Ching. The two trigrams which compose a given hexagram in the I-Ching are composed of three lines each. The top line is always represented as Heaven, the bottom line, Earth, and the middle line, Man. Man must maintain his balance between Heaven and Earth. In T'ai Chi, your head corresponds to the top line in a trigram, always moving lightly as if through the heavens. In this manner, the circulation of Chi moves from the base of the spine to the back of the head, then down the front of the body back to the <u>Tan T'ien</u>, like a river returning to the sea.

The rise is very important. The chin is a little lower and the eye looks forward. To sense a more spiritual movement, we have to raise our head. To be a good exercise, you raise your head. From the base of the spine, the circulation flows up the back to the head. If you raise up your head, the circulation from the back comes up to the crown of your head and comes down--circulating.

We carry something with the head, but relaxed, not stiff. Hanging your head straight, like putting something on your head to carry. Our heads are held as if suspended from above. Something like a piece of string is hanging up your head.

Dropping your head is a very bad habit and makes the movement of no spiritual life. If you drop your head, you cannot see your opponent. Raise your head. It's very important.

If a fighting cock drops his head, it's a sign of defeat and he will run away and the other one will chase after him and pick at his feathers. Also, our practice we always must remember to raise up our head and relax our neck. If we can become accustomed to do this, we can be successful and enjoy ourself. This is spiritual. With the spiritual practice it's interesting and we enjoy more. So 'raise up' so important. Raise up and focus spiritual and you'll find interest and then you'll enjoy the exercise and be happy to do it.

(6) RETURN   To maintain an even balance, movement in one direction is directly related to its opposite (to and fro, up and down, left and right, in and out). <u>Return</u> means balance between substantial and insubstantial movement. In China, we call this balance

between opposites, Yin-Yang. Our legs work like a bow, and our advance and retreat should be controlled from the waist by the spine. Our backs and our arms should be rounded. Inside and outside should be circulating with Chi. It is an awkward thing to do at first, but to and fro, advance and retreat train us to move in Yin-Yang. We should have both hard and soft, substantial and insubstantial in our movements at the same time. In maintaining the balance between Yin and Yang, there should be a constant shift between the substantial and the insubstantial in our movement.

We go forward all full hard, but we have balance - we go back. When you touch my hand, I let go. I sit back. Those ideas are all linked or joined together. Yin-Yang always comes together - not separated; it's balanced. So, doing this exercise is very fine, very fine principle. I go up - sit back. When I sit back, maybe I go the other side, left and right. All is round. All your body is spring-like. Even in the whole body you are spring-like; Yin-Yang, hard and soft, not always hard. You think it's soft, but it's hard. When I relax my hand it's very soft, but you touch it, it's so hard like a rock. This is the job you do--Internal work. It takes a long time to do this. You train yourself. You make up your mind to learn.

Our retreat and advance should be controlled by the waist, by the kidneys. All our movement is wonderful. You don't move the head or shoulders. Our back and arm should be round; round is very important. The arm and back is round.

Whenever you do your standing or your Form, round your arm and round your back and also round your leg. Your leg like a bow is round.

Inside and outside should be circulating with Chi; you practice, you have Chi. If you don't practice, you have no Chi. Suppose you put up your hand and snap your finger. You can feel your Chi in your palm and feel the tip of your finger here; something tickles; you feel that. So, the Chi always comes here and then your fingers like two chopsticks. Understand? It's hard things to know - to and fro, advance and retreat - train us to move Yin-Yang. All round movements have Yin-Yang, hard and soft. Not always hard - sometimes soft, sometimes hard, and this when you learn you understand. Express is hard - conceal is soft. To know the balance of Yin-Yang we should have hard and soft in all our movements at the same time. This is hard to express. When we go to Advanced State we know.

Yin-Yang circle sometimes is a very small circle. The circle doesn't always mean a big circle; sometimes it's very small. If our left side is heavy, our left side will also be empty. Heavy suddenly becomes light and light suddenly becomes heavy. A small circle can do that. Same with the right side. It can be heavy and empty, go and come, come and go. If the opponent raises his hand, you can raise yours higher than opponent. When opponent brings your hand down, you can go down deeper. If attacker brings you forward, you can forward more. If the attacker makes you retreat, you can retreat more.

Therefore, heavy and light should be distinguished. Heavy and light should be understood properly. Therefore, you can get to weight and lightness in every part of your body and the weight and lightness should be in all of your movements, and at the same time you should be linked together and all come together. In all our body and our joints don't make a link to stop or hesitation.

There should be change, one advance and retreat. To make your to and fro more smoothly your Chi should go to your back and conceal inside your bone. Therefore, this is called Sea of Chi - under your stomach. Everything is concealed there: in and out, conceal and express. Although all of this style or form should be empty and heavy, you should have softness. In your movement you should have calmness. Sometimes you don't have movement, but you are moving inside. So, everything is concealed. You can't see. Although you are soft, you have force - up and down, advance and retreat with circularity. That is the principle we should follow in the exercise.

(7) RESTRAIN The mind should be calm, maintaining an inner void. Don't mind how fierce your opponent is. Whatever moves he makes will be seen and interpreted with clarity and quickness when the mind is calm, focused and relaxed. Calmly watch your opponent with an inner stillness. (Look for nothing and see everything; look for something and see nothing). Your mind must be as calm as a mirrored lake which clearly reflects all its surroundings. Calmness and stillness of the mind will provide crystal-clear expression within the idea and timing of your movement. This calmness is needed to meet any opponent's attack, the instant he comes into reachable space. A calm, relaxed mind is equipped with the capacity to think, calculate and be logical with immeasurable speed. Theories concerning the limits of speed, in regards to the physics of the mind, are believed to have numerous phenomena of energy formation that travel faster than light waves. The high speed of psychomotor experience in time, space and force coordination, is integrated by the mind and body with ultra-fast light units of speed when the mind is emptied, relaxed and devoid of preconceived thoughts. Also, body posture and movement alignment, with the goal of perfect balance, is extremely essential in facilitating a calm, inner stillness, while confronting an opponent or any other difficult, stressful situation.

(8) CONCEAL Maintain a comfortable, natural, relaxed mental and physical state of practice. Your body movements are concealed with soft, gentle, even expression, as though you were moving the air. Conceal your force like a bow within the joints and bones with spiral, spring-like focus. Send it out straight as an arrow. Your movement seems not to move. Calmness of the mind provides wonderful harmony in all your movements. It enables you to train your breathing and provides opportunity to control the breathing and express the Chi together with the spirit of the movement and breathing in

unison. For this to take place, however, extraneous thoughts should be excluded and concentration utilized on concealing your inner force by not expressing the applications of the martial art science outwardly. The mind intent with the intrinsic principles of the six combinations and eight methods provides extreme harmony between the body's inner atmosphere (Chi) and the outward expression of the Spirit-movement. Slow, graceful movement occurs naturally and is expressed with exacting accuracy from within the mind intent. If this method of practice is incorporated in one's daily life, stress reduction, lower blood pressure and reduced L.D.L. cholesterol can be realized. Also, negative emotions can give way to a feeling of ease, patience and harmony.

There is a goodness in the forms. As you practice you will find them out. A feather cannot alight, a fly cannot rest, without you being sensitive. I know my enemy's intentions without him knowing mine.

Stand in strict line with gravity. Move lightly and lively with your own will. Your calmness is as a mountain. Your movements like a flowing river. Extreme softness will make extreme strength. In movement there is calmness. Turn your spirit to the void. There is no "I", no myself, and you can move from one world to another with ease and enjoyment. It is all one world.

If you move without thought, you are formless and without feature. You are the natural state. This infinity, this emptiness, is without thought. When you add a thought, then Yin-Yang comes up. Yin-Yang is the mother of all changes.

What are the Six Combinations?

(1) The BODY combines with the MIND (Mind-Intent). Extraneous thoughts should be excluded from the mind and concentration utilized. The mind-intent moves the Chi (inside atmosphere of the body) so that it may sink deeply and penetrate the bones. The mind-intent and Chi must interact in a lively manner in order to achieve both smoothness and circularity.

(2) The MIND combines with the IDEA. Before the MIND directs the movement, you should have a clear IDEA of what to do. Relax the entire body, calm your mind and concentrate on breathing from the diaphragm. The relationship between the mind-intent and the Chi is like an automobile; inside is the driver and the engine. To move the automobile, it will take the mind-intent who is the driver and the Chi who is the engine working and interacting together.

(3) The IDEA combines with the CHI. The IDEA directs the CHI to circulate throughout the body with balanced alignment of T'ai-Chi rooting. The breath must be in unison with the movements of the body. Each meditative movement heightens perception of body awareness and cultivates Chi.

(4) The CHI combines with the SPIRIT. Your Spirit comes up - the Chi comes up. The Spirit low - the Chi low. The Spirit goes left - the Chi goes left. All comes together - combine. Chi should be stimulated and the Spirit should be combined with the Chi and movement. This will cause you more activity and happy to enjoy your movement. Chi works internally and concentrating by Spirit. Spirit is controlled by your calm mind and Spirit directs all the movement at your wishes. And everything come up from internal, so smoothly, calmly, evenly - up and down, to and fro, left and right, like a dragon swimming

in water, in air. The longer you practice the better time you have and more pleasure you get. The longer you practice, the more you find out.

Push the crown point upward, as if the head is suspended from above, ears are listening inward, the tongue is rolled toward the back of the mouth with the teeth and lips lightly touching together. The CHI is concentrated downward into the Tan T'ien and flows smoothly. The breathing is long, slow, smooth, rhythmic and continuously linked to each movement. Do not use CHI alone to move you, but also put your SPIRIT into the movement. SPIRIT and CHI together directs your movements.

(5) The SPIRIT combines with the MOVEMENT. You should put Spirit into movements. Without Spirit, they are dull - but with Spirit, your movements are like a lively dragon: up and down, left and right, in and out. You should understand, it's very important. Chi and Spirit join into one which will help you easy to success - into the Natural State. But in vigor, still not allow you to show out, but conceal in slow motion by calming your mind. And all the parts of your body controlled by Spirit that make you more happy in practice and give you more interest in those who look at you. That's why we practice in a garden. People stop and watch and sometimes ask questions.

You should put your SPIRIT into the MOVEMENTS. Without SPIRIT, the MOVEMENT will be dull. Express each of your movements with your eyes and your crown point raised upward. Move like a lively dragon - up and down, left and right, in and out, allowing all movement to move from the waist. Your movement should be round and smooth. Thus, your movements look both esthetically balanced and lively.

(6) The MOVEMENT combines with the AIR. Until he reaches an advanced level, this is hard for the beginner to understand. Once grasped, one should never practice the exercise without heeding the principle. To move like the AIR is to move effortlessly like a fish swimming, with the least body resistance. All parts of your body must feel the air around you. Only when you are capable of moving through the air around you, coordinating all parts of your body, will you achieve the highest aim of our exercise, which is to achieve the natural state.

24

13) This exercise maintains one's broadminded spirit.

In China we say the broad-minded Chi, but in America Spirit may be substituted for Chi. This means we go toward the good, towards the bright things. This takes time; practice every day.

Before the Republic of China there was the Ching Dynasty. Before the Ching Dynasty, there was the Ming Dynasty. During that time the country nearly collapsed. The Emperor needed a new prime minister and since no one else wanted the job he employed Man-ting-chang, who until that time was undistinguished as a civil servant. Only a small army was left, but he fought valiantly against the Ching. After the wars, Man-ting-chang was captured and the new emperor of China offered him the same job in the new Ching government. He refused, saying that death was his glory, and his duty as a righteous man. Although he was beheaded, his noble act of defiance in the face of death made his enemy, the emperor cry. Man-ting-chang, while in jail, had written a song called the broad-minded spirit song. All Chinese still honor him. Our exercise helps to develop this broad-minded spirit. A broad-minded spirit follows the truth, cools the temper, and finds pleasure and satisfaction in the natural state -- the advanced state.

To explain the reason why we should move towards the advanced state is also in the Bible. Ephesians, Chapter 4, Verses 14 - 16: "That we henceforth be no more children, tossed to and fro, and carried about with every wind of doctrine, by the sleight of men, and cunning craftiness, whereby they lie in wait to deceive; But speaking the truth in love, may grow up into him in all things, which is the head, even Christ: From whom the whole body fitly joined together and compacted by that which every joint supplieth, according to the effectual working in the measure of every part, maketh increase of the body unto the edifying of itself in love."

14) The entire body is elastic - spring-like.

All our muscles are curves. When we move them in correspondence with their design, they help us to obtain movement that is spring-like. Expand and contract, moving slowly in both large and small circles. This is the way to train, and to loosen your muscles.

Once a master of T'ai Chi was fishing in a pond. Someone tried to push him in, but his body was so spring-like, that the aggressor was tossed over the master's shoulders and into the water.

When practicing we should relax. No external strength should be used. Natural force will come up from your bones and from your joints.

15) The beginning of the internal force can be recognized by the opponent.

Your enemy can see and feel your internal force coming, but as soon as they try to grab you, it goes away. First it is hard, then soft. It is deceptive. This internal force is trained from slow, even, linked-together movements. It is especially helped by rooting to the ground, and by always staying balanced during the process of movement.

Spring-like, the force comes and goes. The enemy does not know me, but I know the enemy and when he is going to attack me. I understand, thus I control the fighting situation. I am sure I can win. I am sure the enemy loses.

16) When the exercise is mastered, one's feature and intent are unrecognizable.

The Form becomes formless. The mind is empty -- no idea is shown.

17) Movement to and fro is not revealed.

When you retreat or advance, don't show your feature. It should be smooth and concealed. All movements are rounded in circles. There should never be hesitation. Once you have decided to move, do so evenly, smoothly and gracefully. In this way you train yourself for self-defense. Otherwise, you will resist your own movement and become vulnerable.

18) Relaxing and flexing of movement are self-determined.

(Yin-Yang) All the movements are controlled by your will. When you practice you can do it different ways. If you desire, you can practice peacefully, or else you can practice as if an opponent were in front of you. There are many ways for meditative practice which are associated with this exercise.

19) One must meet attack by being calm.

Being calm is to empty the mind. Being calm is to watch the conditions with clarity and perspective. If we are calm, we can observe well and foresee the attack. Calmness lends wisdom in how exactly to meet the enemy. The greater the trouble, the greater the need for being calm. This calm is concealed. Be without feature.

Lower your weight. Meet the attack with cleverness. Wait like the cat, who springs to catch the mouse. Control the situation. If your attacker is an inner worker, you both have to wait. Smile and talk the truth instead of fighting.

20) The body should be straight in stance.

Don't lean. Be straight. The spine is straight. Some students lean back and that's bad. Some lean forward or to the side. Give the work to the legs. When you are straight, there is greater blood circulation to the brain.

> *Raise up your head.*
> *Relax the shoulders.*
> *Lower the elbows.*
> *Relax the chest.*
> *Weight is lowered.*

Eyes straight ahead, forward.
These are important.

21) The opponent sees no resistance in your stance, but this is false for you are concealed.

When people see such slow, soft practice they say, "How can this be used for self-defense?" But, because of internal strength, we can. Because our joints and muscles, indeed all the body is loosened by slow and even training, there is no hindrance to our movement; so slow makes fast. Practice with concentration and relaxation; you will act naturally.

If in the case of emergency you must use T'ai Chi for self-defense, then like guerrilla war tactics, yield at first, but attack at the end.

22) If one does not practice regularly, then do not face the enemy.

From this we see a warning that we should practice every day. Unless we practice every day, we obtain nothing, neither the benefits of health nor self-defense. Don't be lazy. If you are lazy, you cannot meet the enemy; also, you will get fat. Take your exercise every day as you take your food. Your health will improve. Practice makes perfect. Remember.

23) When in motion one is still rooted.

Rooted is very important. Our first lessons are in "walking" and "rowing the boat" which helps us to have good rooting. Practice "walking" and "rowing" daily for two or three years. The more you practice, the more graceful you are in your exercise. It is the same with tall buildings; the foundation must be good. Build on rock, not sand. Rooting is not found in T'ai Chi, but in Hsing-I. In ancient days in China, students of Hwa Yu took three years to train in rooting, before they began to learn the Form.

24) Do not overextend yourself to the opponent.

Keep your gravity firmly centered. The knees should not over-extend the toes. Legs are slightly bowed. Save a place to retreat to. Deeply meditate the movement. If overextended, the Chi will be weak and it gives your attacker a chance to attack you. Overextension indicates the greed of your will with a desire to have an advantage to knock down your enemy.

25) Judge the chance and take the opportunity.

In pushing hands, we call this the "chance to follow" and move in time. We develop good judgment by sticking, by turning with the waist, by measuring the distance. Don't overextend. Raise up the head, straighten the spine, lower the weight, root firmly. Wait for your chance. As soon as there is a chance suitable for you to attack, attack at once.

26) One strikes with internal force before the opponent advances with strength.

We watch for the chance with our mind, then once we see our opportunity, we move swift like the arrow.

27) When the opponent is hard, then one is soft.

When your opponent is hard, then you are soft. Yield to force when it reveals itself. When your opponent is soft, you are hard. If your opponent is quicker than you are, and his strength has reached you, yield further. Yield, and lead your opponent into emptiness.

28) Although the opponent is busy, one stays calm awaiting him.

If your enemy's strength is sent out, you should use soft force.

29) He is busy attacking you; you should calmly wait.

Don't bother how busy your opponent is when he comes to attack you. You should wait calmly, and watch for the chance to meet him.

30) When to attack or to protect is according to one's decision.

With a calm mind, you can do whatever you like to attack or to protect. During this fighting time, there should be no fear; only calm. If I can, I am quick to stop the opponent's strength. If my opponent is quick, I yield to guide his advancing into emptiness.

31) Take the first opportunity and be quicker than the opponent.

If one has practiced well, then one's muscles and joints should be loose enough to respond quickly and easily.

32) Always concentrate on the situation.

One important principle of T'ai Chi is: If the people don't move, I do not move. If they wish to move, I move at once. I am quicker than my attacker. I take the advantage. When they start to move their strength (like drawing back in a punch), I attack at once! I stop it before it starts. This principle is put forward in the story of the little girl who put out a fire when it was small, only a spark. The story of the Dutch boy with his finger in the dike is also based on the principle of stopping before it starts.

I stop the strength of the enemy by taking the first chance. In Chinese we call "Stopping the strength" Chit King. We must train to be loose in the muscles and joints so we can be quick to stop.

When the opponent is hard, then I am soft. I yield. When they are soft, I am hard! If the opponent is quicker than you and his strength has reached you, yield. I yield and lead my enemy into an empty space. I guide his advances into emptiness.

It is important to concentrate. Pay attention to the environment before his strength and after his strength. We can see the two fishes, hard and soft, busy and calm. If you concentrate, you will see the way. We are naturally quicker than our enemy. There is no more hindrance, no tightness, no tension. We move naturally; we can attack or protect as we wish.

33) Conceal one's force like the bow: round and ready to spring.

Make your body round outside and round your force inside. In Hsing-I we train the three brackets (round spaces).

1) Shoulders: relax your chest--force travels to elbows and then to fingers.

2) Backs of hands and feet: rooting firmly, grip the ground.

3) Upper and lower teeth: joined together slightly, the force travels to your bones and blood vessels, tendons and nerves.

34) Attack as the arrow - quick and straight.

This means that the inner force comes forth at once, because the arms and hands are rounded. The hand is circles, but the force moves straight ahead. The force comes from the whole body. This is good for pushing hands and self-defense. Remember to balance all sides. Your weight goes down to your abdomen. Raise your head. Lower your shoulders and elbows.

35) One should thoroughly understand the principle of Yin-Yang.

(Refer to the following principle.)

36) Both the Yin and Yang flow in and out, hard and soft, and are of mutual use.

We cannot have one without the other. When the whole body is spring-like, the Yin and Yang flow together.

The student may ask: "How can we make a heavy foot turn?" You can! Grip with the heel and turn the toes and the heavy foot will be light enough to turn.

In the diagram of the two fishes, both Yin and Yang (substantiality and insubstantiality) are equally represented. There is a firmness concealed in softness: there is activity concealed in inactivity. Therefore in Yin-Yang we have hard-soft, in-out, up-down, left-right, heavy-light, etc.

In the beginning of the exercise the first movements neutralize the opponent's attack. The second movements turn the opponent away. This shows Yin and Yang working together. (Up and down.)

Yin-Yang are of mutual use: in and out, visible and invisible, suddenly here and suddenly there.

Such kind of activity is used in warfare by the guerrillas. There is a story from the beginning of the Hon Dynasty. In the Chan Dynasty the Emperor built a great wall, but the Emperor was very cruel to the people. During the reign of the Emperor's son there were two rebellions: the Chor Rebellion and the Hon Rebellion. The leader of the Chor was a famous warrior with a fierce army, but the leader of the Hon Shun used the principle of

Yin-Yang to defeat the fierce enemy. Hon Shun became the leader of the army. He decreed that the bad roads of Chan must be repaired. When the fierce warrior of the Chor heard about it, he paid no attention to the wise general. "He is a foolish fellow - it will take a year at least!" So, Chor spent the year drinking and feasting. But Hon Shun moved his army along the secret route of Chen-Chong to his enemy's camp. By such sudden attack he won the war. He used the "short-cut" way.

In Europe there is another tale of sudden and surprise attack. The Italians took no notice of their enemy's advance along a dangerous route. Napoleon and the French forces did take the risk of crossing the Alps and by using such a "short-cut" way, they won the war.

This is the way of Yin-Yang: visible and invisible, suddenly here and suddenly there. We are hard when the opponent is soft. We retreat when the opponent advances. We bend and stretch when we need to.

37) Breathing is regular from the bottom of the abdomen to the heart.

In China, the "heart" is where the breath moves to when we inhale "naturally." All breathing should therefore be "natural," according to one's needs at the moment the breath is taken or expended.

Generally, you inhale when you raise or lift your body, and you exhale when you sink, or lower your body. But this should never be considered an absolute. Breathe naturally according to your needs.

38) This cyclic up and down breathing smoothes the Chi.

When we are breathing naturally, we are relaxed. When we are relaxed the Spirit combines with the Chi, and all our movements will flow together in natural circles. Natural breathing is essential to the internal aspect of the exercise.

39) Be calm as the resting Buddhist.

The exercise is so quiet, it seems not to move. In practice you should move as slowly, and as fluidly as possible; as if you were moving while standing in water. This trains our patience, and strengthens our internal force.

40) Move like a dragon rising from hibernation.

The long-rested dragon has stored vast amounts of energy for movement with great inner force. When you move, move evenly, and without stopping a little at a time, but like the dragon, slowly, with inner force, and always with a strong idea behind you. This <u>inner force</u> is concealed strength.

41) This calmness appears empty but there is something within.

When you are calm while practicing, your quiet appearance is deceptive. It looks like nothing. Your mind is empty: free from all internal dialogue, and you act from an idea concealed inside. This idea holds our hard and soft Chi, our Spirit, and our Geng. This idea is born from our <u>Will</u>, and our Will provides our direction to follow.

42/43) The internal force which is wonderfully rewarding can be suddenly concealed, and suddenly expressed.

There is self-control in what we wish to do. Self-control comes from our emptied mind. When an empty mind judges that there is a chance to attack, the order is given to the internal force to express itself suddenly. The opposite holds true when there is the will to conceal.

44) All breathing shall be natural.

A cat appears to be very quiet while waiting for the chance to pounce upon its prey, when actually there is concentrated internal movement. You would never realize this from the cat's slow and even breathing. Like the cat, during this period of waiting for the chance to attack, our breathing should be natural. Naturalness is the highest aim of our exercise. If you find there is tension in any part of your body, even in the breath, you are not in a "natural state." Instead, you are inhibited and unwillful. All should be natural. Breathing "naturally" aids our Will to act by exercising our internal muscles.

Remember:
Raise your head lightly, lifting up, and out.
Lower your shoulders and elbows.
Keep your weight in your lower abdomen.
Shift your weight into one leg.
Sit upon your hip joint.
Move steadily, evenly, slowly.
Straighten and relax your body.
Do your exercise every day.

All this will enable you to move in the "natural state."

45) Yield to heavy attack.

In hard stuff, force is always used against force, but in our soft exercise we teach how to yield.

Let your attacker advance as he desires. Don't mind how he comes. Yield. Don't be in his way. Guide him towards his desired direction. The more force with which he advances, the *further he will go where you desire. Thus causing him to lose his balance, you guide him into emptiness. When his balance is lost, you move to attack. Only a small force need be used since he is moving without control and with great force.*

The T'ai Chi principle is "We use four ounces of force to push away 1,000 ratties of strength." I yield to the heavy attack; guide him to the empty. At the moment he loses his balance I use four ounces of force. That much is sufficient to make my attacker fall.

In battle the enemy will sometimes play the same trick. While the enemy sends old soldiers to attack, the defending army issues its full command against the old soldiers, and are thus guided away from the real strength. Then, the general sneaks in the back way once the defending army has depleted its strength against a worthless opponent.

46) Every action is self-initiated.

In the art of self-defense, how to meet my attacker is <u>my</u> decision.

Sometimes we do not use "yield;" sometimes we use "stop," and counter his advance with power derived from our Chi. But if we are not well trained, we had best run away from fighting. Our muscles and blood vessels must be relaxed and loose in order to respond either by "yielding" or by "stopping" the attack. For this, daily practice is necessary.

47) Distribution of weight between one leg and the other is clearly distinguished.

The shifting of weight from one leg to another is required quite often in our exercise. Always, when one leg is heavy, the other should be light. The heavy leg gives balance to the <u>whole</u> body, while the light leg should be so light that there appears to be nothing on which to move. If this principle of light and heavy is not followed, you will make yourself easily "beatable" because you will have no rooting.

48) The body is of both yin and yang, both empty and solid.

When the body changes direction, there should be a corresponding shift in weight from one to the other leg. To move contrary to this principle is to deny the principle of Yin and Yang (light and solid).

49) By emptying oneself, the opponent's force is led to a void.

Since you remove the object (yourself) towards which your opponent's attack is directed by changing your center of gravity, you guide the force of your opponent's attack to a <u>void</u>. The heavier, the more forceful his attack, the greater the void: thus the greater his fall.

50) If the enemy retreats, stick with quick advance.

If your enemy is clever enough to realize that his advance is useless, and thus retreats, you should stick to him with quick advance.

To accomplish this, daily practice, with close attention paid to loosening the hip and spine is absolutely necessary. If your hip and spine are well trained by moving slowly, fluidly and calmly, you should be capable of advancing or retreating more quickly than your opponent.

51) The legs should be curved like a bow.

This is the balance of our advance and retreat. If our legs curve like a bow, we can advance and retreat smoothly, evenly, and circularly.

52) Advancing and retreating use force derived from the spine.

In the T'ai Chi principles it is said, "The most important part of the exercise is the spine." We should then take care when doing our exercise to have all movement issued from the spine.

53) The arms and back should be round as if hugging.

In Hsing-I, the shoulders should be rounded by slightly hollowing the upper chest, which *allows the circulation of Chi to flow to the tips of your fingers. In Pa Kua you are instructed to hollow the chest, thereby creating a bow with the two shoulders. This is necessary for developing Chi and Geng; the inner atmosphere and inner force.*

All our movements should be circular. This principle should be followed at all times - especially for beginners. The analogy of the rounded bow strung for the arrow is useful here: as the bow is rounded, creating greater "emptiness," more force is stored for the arrow's release.

54) Circulate your Chi from the inside to the outside.

Beginners should take notice of this sentence: "Circulate your Chi from the inside to the outside," because the Chi is not an external creation from something which was not always an internal part of you. Chi lies dormant in your Tan T'ien until you create the necessary physiological conditions necessary for it to rise, and flow through the body. If the beginner practices every day for a month or so, the Chi will gradually rise. But only if the chest is hollowed, and the body is rounded.

They say the Chi inside atmosphere should be stimulated and the Spirit of the vigor should be concealed. Stimulated should be remembered in all our exercise, even in standing. You see people standing not moving, but it is moving. How to move? Stimulated. The Five Word Song said "seems as not to move." Seems not to move but it moves inside and comes up and moves outside. But we should move inside slightly. Don't quick. If quick, that means we have no time to do it. It is better for you single. You practice exercise alone and can do details slowly and you feel something when you improve and you find out something you haven't had before. You cannot find out in one day or one week or a month; at least find something. As it moves so slightly inside stimulated, that it does not show up. They cannot see it. This causes stimulation and such slow movement inside that can keep your circulation going round and freely. It helps your circulation. This is the inner work.

The movement should move evenly, regularly - up and down, left and right, slowly, smoothly, without strength and continuously. Therefore, the Chi can rise up to the top of the head and come down to the Sea of Chi. As an example, as in a calm lake it should require the wind as the inner atmosphere called Chi to help to the surface of the lake move slowly and make lively water - not still water, lively. It's not still water because still water would cause to grow some worms in it and mosquitoes in it and many germs in it, etc. Does no good. So the Creator is wonderful. The lake looks so calm. It works slowly. It's stimulated from inside. It's no good if it doesn't move. It's not good to the lake. So, the stimulation in a movement gives a great help to our body in circulating, making the muscle join, active, strong and increase the inner force, the Geng, more and more. It gives a good help to our health and self defense as well. The Chi, inner atmosphere, should be stimulated in such a way.

55/56) Stop trivial thoughts and concentrate on your movement, as if facing a difficult enemy.

To stop trivial thoughts is an important term, which has been explained in the first statement: "Empty your mind." Only when the mind is empty (free from internal dialog) can you concentrate on each of your movements, while fully enjoying the exercise for its inherent peace and joy.

In order to make progress in the exercise, you must concentrate on the "idea" of how to meet the attack with your movement, as if you were facing a difficult enemy. Concentration upon <u>application</u> insures the correctness of each movement and develops the internal aspect of the exercise. The result of movement, directed by the Will, is good Chi.

57) Your eyes move about like lightning.

In the T'ai Chi principles they talk about the eye being like the cat at the moment it is about to catch the mouse. The cat's eyes are like windows through which we observe the cat's will (intent) before the strike. Therefore, we have to pay attention and watch our own movement - here and there like the cat's eye watching his prey.

58) Your spirit watches in all four directions (front, back, left, right).

This sentence is also talking about the eye. The Spirit of your eye watches in all directions because the enemy will come from different directions to attack you.

59) Your footing should be 40% to the front and 60% to the rear.

The rear footing does more than the front. The rear has to support the whole body forward and backward. Therefore, training to stand firmly on your hind leg is very important for beginners. Your front leg gets 40%, but both legs are interchangeable.

60) The hands are 30% to the front and 70% to the rear.

People do not understand. When attacking, they use all strength to go forward, but this is not our principle. In this soft exercise, we need 70% at the rear hand. If we draw our attacker to advance with 70%, the enemy will more easily lose his balance. Only 30% on the other hand is needed to attack our enemy, and the enemy will suffer double weight from our blow because his heavy attack is helped to advance by my 70%. At the time to

The Chinese Five Word Song

use 30% to attack him he could be badly hurt. To protect uses 70%. To attack uses 30%. This is the principle of our exercise.

61) The feature of the movement is like swimming in the water.

At one point during the development of the Hwa Yu style of T'ai Chi, the exercise was called <u>Swimming Boxing</u>. This was so because the movement up or down, to the right or to the left was always slow, fluid and calm, giving the appearance of moving through water or air.

62/63) Movement is light, like a fairy in the clouds.

Because our movement is so light, and gentle, you should look like a beautiful fairy, dancing in the clouds.

64) The idea is very great, but there is nothing; it is like a great void.

Your movements should arise from a strong idea. To fully open yourself with movement means that the idea is completely executed; your body closes smoothly so as to cooperate with all within your body. Your moving has been so light that nothing seems unnatural. This open movement appears to be nothing more than a great void, wherein nothing is contained. Yet your idea has been fully realized, then has withdrawn as if nothing has happened. All this belongs only to the most advanced student.

65) The idea of the movement is like a fierce tiger.

This describes your concentration on moving with good expression. When you advance to attack, your concealed idea has revealed itself in movement like a fierce tiger.

66) The calmness of Chi is very gentle.

Movement, although fierce like the tiger's, is not aggressive. The Chi is gentle. Remaining calm in a dangerous situation is being true to your Chi, and thus enables us to take care of ourselves; when we are calm we exercise caution and are able to look after everything that could harm us.

In dangerous situations, most people manifest their fear and confusion by immediately resisting the situation, but I remain calm, available, yet not available, and true to my Chi, so that I might sense how my opponent is going to attack me. Because I remain calm I am adaptable so that I can move hard and soft at the same time - depending on what is called for by the circumstances.

The T'ai Chi classics maintain "This is the way of a hero who cannot be overcome." A slang saying is "Carefulness can help us maintain our boat for 10,000 years." Carefulness is the truth of our Chi.

67) Once the enemy is on the offensive, the enemy is defeated.

Always, we are prepared. With caution we meet our enemy. Beware every minute. Once the enemy is offensive he makes his own trouble. If your enemy becomes defensive, wait - do not act, wait for his advance, then anticipate and move quicker.

68) The inner strength controls the Five Terminals and the Nine Joints.

Five terminals: *2 palms, 2 arches, top of head*

Nine joints: *2 wrist joints2 elbow joints*
       2 shoulder joints   *(there are others*
       1 hip joint   *such as the neck,*
       2 knee joints   *ankles, toes, etc.)*

What this means is that <u>all</u> the joints work together; they are all linked together. The Geng moves through the bones and unites the body into one movement. If calm, all is calm. If active, all is active.

Beginners will move each part individually. But soon, they must work to join the movements together. Relax the whole body. Make the internal force grow from soft to strong and then to the natural state. The flow circulates from the head down to the rooting. Carry on the flow in a natural way. Thus, advanced progress can be made.

69) If one wants to learn, then one must practice frequently.

The inner force can control the 5 terminals and 9 joints. If you make up your mind to practice, you should do so every day. Rely upon yourself. Don't be lazy. If you practice frequently, you will advance to the higher standard. Relax and empty the mind.

We have a Chinese proverb about a man whom everyone called "Foolish." "Foolish" wanted to make a road from his house straight through the mountain to the market and thus avoid the winding roads over the mountain. Enlisting the help of his sons and grandsons, he worked at tunneling through the mountain. All the neighbors laughed and called him "Foolish," but with work every day he accomplished his purpose. You must practice daily if you seek to accomplish your purpose.

70) In this way, studying and practice of the exercise enables a deeper progress to be made. From the door to the hall to the chamber with one's master.

We progress step by step, deeper and deeper in understanding our exercise. In ancient China there is a name given to those students who practiced frequently and hard: these were the "chamber students." They were close to the master and were of high standards. Less advanced students were called "hall students." Even lesser ones were termed "door students." The chamber student's progress, however, is ceaseless: advance without end.

71) When the exercise is mastered, one's inner force can be concealed or expressed at will.

This sentence refers to the Geng, or the inner force. This internal force comes from a relaxed state of being. Without relaxation, the Geng cannot develop. When we have truly achieved a state of relaxation, we gain Geng strength. It takes time to master the Geng. Once mastered, this force can be released at will. When we practice our exercise, the more we practice, the more we gain. Like people who dig in the mine, the deeper you dig, the more you are apt to find.

72) Focus the Spirit to discover the Truth.

From this sentence we understand that Spirit is very important. In this manner we discover many valuable things. In much the same manner are priceless gems sought. They are difficult to find, but once found, we readily agree that our efforts have been worthwhile.

Both our <u>Spirit</u>, and our <u>Idea</u> must direct our exercise. Let all your body be light and filled with <u>Spirit</u>. It is this <u>Spirit</u> which controls the whole movement, and all its changes.

Let the <u>Spirit</u> be calm, and concentrated inside the body. Pay attention to it as you would pay attention to a light shower of rain.

The <u>Idea</u> becomes refined and combines with the <u>Chi</u>. The <u>Spirit</u> and the <u>Chi</u> go to and fro together. The movement of the <u>Spirit</u> should be continuously in a tipsy state, smooth, concentrated and light, like one who sleeps on water, or like one who swims on land.

Go calmly toward the universal; lightly and spiritually, but with a fixed <u>Idea</u> toward your movements.

73) This harmonious exercise combines all the movement.

The most beneficial quality about our exercise is that all our movement is harmonious. No one part of your body moves irrespective of another. Rather each part of the body moves in combination with the whole. Like an automobile, when the drive shaft of the car is moving, all the parts of the car move in concert. All movement becomes one movement.

74) The quietness and emptiness of this exercise separate one from worldly things.

These combinations of movement are entirely different from the exercises which worldly people do since our stress is upon quietness, and emptiness. The world likes to fight, but this is not the main point of our exercise, and if we mix up the exercise with the worldly Kung Fu, we cannot achieve good results.

There is a story from ancient China about a man who tried to draw a tiger. He failed, and his picture ended up looking like a dog. Therefore, make up your mind to advance according to the principles.

There is another story about a certain City A, who admired City B because the people of B could walk so bravely. So the people of City A sent ten boys of their own City into B to learn from them how to walk bravely. When the boys returned, the people anxiously inquired about what they had learned. The boys lay down on the ground and crawled. The town laughed at them, for they had learned the wrong way.

Our exercise is not for copying, or for fast secrets.

75/76) Remember all progress towards the truth of this exercise is very delicate.

This is one of the principles you will discover. There is a small, tender thing that fine-hearted people alone can find. It is not for the rough-minded people to possess. Calm your mind when you practice and you will discover that you are your own teacher.

77) The idea of movement is to seem not to move - achieving fluidness.

The Idea which propels your movement is so slow, calm and fluid, that even while you are moving, you appear not to be moving. This kind of movement is required so that all your muscles and joints will become loose, so you will be capable of moving fast when necessary.

78) One's calmness combines with the Idea.

Slowness is not only slow, but slow with the Idea, and the Chi is force behind each slow movement. This becomes meditation through movement.

79) Cease all thoughts, and your Chi will become calm naturally.

How can the Chi go with the movement? Well! You should cease all thoughts, then your Chi will become calm, and will naturally combine with your Idea.

80) Quietly maintain the "great emptiness."

"Quietly" gives you power: therefore you must maintain the "great emptiness" at all times.

81) One's basic foundation is built through this exercise.

There are four steps in focusing the Spirit to discover the truth:

(1) MOVEMENT Make up your mind to discover the state of the outer movement. When the truth of this is found, the Idea will be to seem not to move.

(2) CALMNESS The Idea of one's Will is concealed in calmness.

(3) QUIET OUR CHI By quieting all our thoughts.

(4) MAINTAINING This state is the highest standard of THE GREAT EMPTINESS happiness and enjoyment of the physical world.

82) In this exercise, all valuable points are concealed.

In Chinese, this reads: All your valuable pearls and jade are concealed.

83) It is hard to learn: no, it is not.

The important point is whether you make up your mind to discover or not.

84) It looks easy at first, but it is not easy.

If one has no confidence, you get no benefit. We must practice every day with confidence. Practice makes perfect.

85) If one's mind is made up to learn, then there will be success.

To make up your mind to learn is a prerequisite for studying. Through volition, even while enduring hardship, one can overcome all obstacles. This is the only way to learn. This point is illustrated in a Chinese parable called To Grind the Iron on the Stone to Make a Needle.

There was a famous poet in the Tong Dynasty by the name of Lee Pak. When he was young he liked wandering about, taking pleasure when he wanted. One day he met an old woman who was grinding a piece of iron on a stone. Lee Pak asked her: "What's the use?" The old woman answered, "I want this piece of iron to grind down into a needle." Lee Pak was greatly moved by her words. He returned home and made up his mind to struggle with his studies. Finally he became one of the great poets of his generation.

86) In this world there is nothing of real difficulty.

When we make up our minds to practice the exercise, we have surpassed the only real difficulty. There is nothing left to do but to act on our decision. Once we act, we begin the journey of five thousand miles.

87) To learn, one must be sincere and determined.

Determination is to follow one's choice, having made up your mind to devote yourself willingly to what you have chosen. To be sincere and to be determined are necessary attributes for every student. If you have these, you can be a good student. Listen to your teacher and honor him. If your mind is absent from learning, you cannot hear what your teacher teaches you and you cannot see what the teacher shows you. You cannot succeed; you only waste your time. A student who is not devoted to the work at hand has the heart and mind of a tourist.

88) To learn correctly depends on long frequent practice and on your wisdom.

The success of this exercise depends on long, frequent practice and, most importantly, on the depth of your wisdom gained from calming both body and mind which gives rise to your dormant Chi. Meditate on the movement inside and outside of your body. This is the way to reach the high standard of the natural state.

89) This exercise was invented by Ch'en Hsi-I of Hwa Yu.

The Hwa Yu is the highest peak of the Hwa Shan mountain range. Hwa Shan means "beautiful mountains." This exercise was developed in the northwest of China.

Hsi-I (same as Chen Hsi-I) was a Taoist of the Sung Dynasty (960 - 1274 AD) and was also excellent in the defensive arts, both inner and outer.

In the beginning of the Sung Dynasty, the emperor of the Sung (Chiu Hon Yun) asked Hsi-I to assist him to fight against another king and gain all of China under his control. Hsi-I refused to do so because he was a Taoist. At last a bet was made over a chess game. Hsi-I had a calm mind and he won the game. Henceforth, the Hwa Shan was given to Hsi-I, and during the Sung Dynasty no crown rent was due. Hsi-I enjoyed the natural world of the mountains, and he devoted his mind to study and invention. He chose a few worthy people for his pupils, and because of the few in number, Hwa Yu became a secret art. The Five Word Song is the essential principle. It is to encourage the learners, and was written by Li Tung Fung, Hsi-I's first pupil of Hwa Yu.

90) The student of Hwa Yu should practice every day. This is most important.

Practice every day. If you don't you cannot gain anything. Practice makes perfect. The more you practice, the more you gain. Then you can understand what internal Kung Fu is. It is not only the outside. It is the whole body combined to move as one. Against all difficulty, practice frequently and with patience, and you will obtain a result. Occasional practice leads nowhere.

There is a story about Mencius, the philosopher, who visited the state of Chai. He spoke with the prince who was very indecisive and needed encouragement to stick to anything. He couldn't empty his mind and he would always listen to the critical and conflicting opinions of those around him. Mencius tired of the prince's weakness and spoke to him frankly: "You are not wise. In this universe things that grow need light. You let them have light for only one day, then you put them away for ten days. How can they grow when they are laid away in the freezer?"

Mencius went on to say: "I have been with you for only a short period, but when you are near me you have a good idea. When I leave you, ill-intentioned people come in and influence you. You forget what you've thought when I was with you. What can help you? When you learn to play a game of chess, concentration and patience are necessary. But so too is practice." From this story we glean that whatever we want to learn, we must first overcome hardship, then a concentrated period of time must be devoted to our study. In China there is a saying: One day in the sun and ten days in the freezer cannot succeed.

91) There must be concentration of Spirit and Idea (Will).

In internal Kung Fu physical strength is never used; instead, the Idea is strong, and that Idea directs the movement. The Idea and the Chi must combine before you act. However, if we pay attention only to the Chi and the Idea, it will be dull. Therefore, above Chi and above Idea we have "Spirit." Use the Spirit to guide the Chi and the Idea and to make the whole exercise move in Spirit. The Spirit is essential; Spirit above all leads you to the natural state. In the physical world, let the Spirit guide the Idea and the Chi to move (from beginning to end) in stillness, softness and slowness. This is the internal Kung Fu.

92) All the joints of the body move together.

We should take notice of these three steps:

> 1. *Boxing requires movement, but first the internal requires stillness.*

> 2. *To defeat the enemy requires strength, but first the internal requires softness.*

> 3. *Fighting requires speed, but first the internal requires slowness.*

These steps: stillness, softness and slowness are all the joints of the body moving together.

93) When contact is made, the inner force comes forth at once.

This is the second step after we learn the Form. Whenever our hand connects with our imaginary attacker, our inner force comes forth at once. The imagined feature becomes reality when needed.

From abstract to actual. This imagining force uses Idea instead of strength. All the movements are controlled by the imagination. This exercises the mind. The Form must be known well. Then we can understand how to use our <u>Geng</u> (the force that comes from inside the bone). When this is known there is a third step: the natural state.

Therefore, when we practice daily, we should move naturally, as if we were floating in water. Our movements should circle slowly, calmly and lightly. Put all the weight under the stomach. This is <u>sinking the Chi in the sea</u>. In Chinese, the Sea of Chi is called the <u>Tan T'ien</u>, and is located about one and one-half inches below the navel.

The slowness of the movement makes it look like stillness. When the movement is extended, it seems <u>not</u> to be so.

We should make circles inside and outside our body. Inside, from the <u>Tan T'ien</u>, Chi circulates to all parts of the body. The outside is only a physical manifestation of the inside movement. This trains our body to be spring-like.

All the inner force comes from the joints; it is concealed there. When we move forward , move straight like a flying arrow. The starting point of the movement is the spine. The shoulders should be relaxed and the inner force should come out from the backbone. This is the whole body moving at once.

In Hsing-I, we get the following explanation of how to move circularly by observing the three raise-ups:

1.   Raise our head - by straightening and lifting the
        cervical vertebrae of the neck. The circulation

        will then go to the top of our head, and this will
        help the mental process.

2.   Raise the palm forward (as if to push) - the Chi
        will flow to the tip of our fingers, which will
        cause our inner force to be stronger.

3.   Raise up our tongue - to the roof of the mouth.
        This gives us more energy, as it transmits the
        Chi from the back portion of the body (yang)
        over the head, and down the front portion (yin)
        of our body - then back down to the Tan T'ien.
        This is called "sinking the Chi."

The Three Brackets

1.   The two shoulders should be round
2.   Back of hand and arch of foot bracket
3.   Teeth bracket

The Three Rounds

1. Back bone round
2. Chest round
3. Tiger-mouth round -- hands cupped, leaving
    space between the thumb and forefinger

The Three Smarts

1. In the mind
2. The eye
3. The hands

The Three Low-Downs

1. Chi
2. Shoulder
3. Elbow

94) This gives no opportunity for the opponent to escape.

The inner force is like a fierce tiger. No escape is possible when, with the speed of lightning, an attack is issued by the whole body.

But to achieve this inner force, we must work hard in the beginning. At first the arms will tire from the exercise; later, and after much practice, they will be like steel, possessing Geng strength.

Your legs will feel hardship. Oh, my bones! You will experience much pain while you train your legs to rest like trees rooted deep within the earth. Once trained, however, you will stand sturdily like a rooted tree.

The body will be relaxed and flexible; it will move lightly when turning. There will be no hindrance inside. This takes much training. Overcome your difficulties by practicing every day.

95) The opponent thinks you are relaxed, but you are not relaxed (Inner Force).

Don't think that your relaxed state is soft <u>without</u> force. Although your body is soft outside, your inner force is not at all soft. The internal work is accomplished by training the inner force up and down, left and right, frontward and backward, without stopping. The form is like a swimming dragon at play. The inner force is so fierce that once the enemy makes his first move, the enemy is defeated.

The inner force is so great it cannot be described by words.

96) The opponent thinks you are tense, but there is no strength.

Don't make yourself tense, especially when you are in danger. There is a famous story in China about a well-known prime minister named Chi Geh Leung.

Once, five heavy attacks were being waged against his country by fierce enemies. All the people of the country were trembling with fear. Nobody knew what step to take. The king relied on Geh Leung as the only man who could settle the matter.

Leung was nowhere to be found. The king himself rode to Leung's mansion and asked the servant where he was. The servant explained that Leung was in the internal garden. What was he doing? The servant further explained that Leung was watching the goldfish and should not be disturbed. No one had dared go near him for many days.

The king walked to the internal garden where the prime minister watched the goldfish. Although he stood patiently at Leung's side for a long time, he was not noticed. Finally, the king said, "My lord, are you well?"

The prime minister turned his head and saw the king. He knelt before the king according to tradition and said, "I am alright." Astonished by Leung's response, the king inquired, "Do you know five fierce enemies have surrounded our borders?" The prime minister replied that he had known this for some time and asked the king whether he had any plan to settle this trouble. "All the country is trembling," the king urged. "No one has any plans."

Leung replied: "I have come up with plans, but I cannot arrive at the final plan. I am disturbed. So I must watch the goldfish swimming. I have some idea of what to do, but it's not perfect."

The king apologized and the prime minister went to the palace with the king. As expected, five plans were carried out to counter the five enemies.

97) All the movement is balanced in a circular fashion.

If your movements are unbalanced, it is very easy to fall down. The balanced movement is firm and does not fall easily.

That's why in #20 it is said: The body should be straight in stance; and in #23: When in motion, one is still rooted: and in #59, #60: Footing is 40% in front and 60% to the rear; and hands are 30% in front and 70% to the rear.

The principles of T'ai Chi also mention: If you go up, you go down. Go to the front, go to the back; left and right. This is the proof that all movements must be balanced. Don't forget.

When we move to balance on all sides, the primary movement comes from the spine and from the footing. This is the real Kung Fu. When the spine moves - all the body moves. When the spine stops - all movement stops. From the principles of T'ai Chi we know: Once moving, all the body moves together. Once quiet, all is quiet. Pay attention to the spine every minute.

Also, the stomach should be loose and relaxed and the Chi will go through the body. If there is relaxation in the stomach, balance is easy.

98) The Chi should be controlled to flow in and out as in a spiraling circle.

> *#14 - The entire body is elastic-spring-like.*

> *#92 - All the joints of the body move together.*

> *#97 - All movement is balanced in a circular*
> *fashion.*

Now, the balance is not only forward and backward, but upward and downward at the same time like a screw. The Chi is controlled at the same time up and down, in and out. Muscles and joints move together by the control of the Chi. This spiraling circle makes the body spring-like.

99) Do not be afraid of the opponent.

To remain fearless, you must be well practiced in every movement. Through initial hardship you will gain something that will make you more than healthy and strong. Your arms will be like steel bars; your footing will be like a huge tree rooting deeply into the earth. Who can push you down? Who can attack you? You are not afraid.

100) Open and close oneself and be able to yield and stick.

Opening and closing of the feature is important. When you are open, you should be prepared to attack. When you close, you should be protecting yourself. If the door is too wide, your enemy can come in. If the door is too narrow, your enemy can close you up. Pay attention to attack and protect. The following principles help us in this work:

> #20.   *The body should be straight in stance.*

> #30.   *When to attack or protect is according to one's decision.*

> #32.   *Always concentrate on the situation.*

> #36.   *Both the Yin and Yang flow in and out, hard and soft, and are of mutual use.*

> #41.   *The calmness appears empty, but there is something within.*

> #42/43. *The Internal force which is wonderfully rewarding can be suddenly concealed, and suddenly expressed.*

> #44.   *All breathing should be natural.*

> #46.   *Every action is self-initiated.*

> #53.   *The arms and back should be round as if hugging.*

#54.   *Circulate your Chi from inside to outside.*

#55.   *Stop trivial thoughts and concentrate on your movement --*

#56.   *as if facing a difficult enemy.*

#58.   *Your spirit watches in all four directions (front, back, left, right).*

#65.   *The idea of the movement is like a fierce tiger.*

#66.   *The calmness of Chi is very gentle.*

#67.   *Once the enemy is on the offensive, the enemy is defeated.*

#75/76. *Remember all progress towards the truth of this exercise is very delicate.*

#91.   *There must be concentration of Spirit and Idea (Will).*

#92.   *All the joints of the body move together.*

#93.   *When contact is made, the inner force comes forth at once.*

#94.   *This gives no opportunity for the opponent to escape.*

101) Watch for the enemy's weak point...

The weak points of the enemy do not follow the principles of the Five Word Song. You can see it. For example:

#17 - Movement is not revealed. If the enemy is weak, his movement is revealed.

#20 - Body not straight. It leans to one side or other.

#22 - Not practice regularly: hand movements are dull - there is no hand smart.

#23 - Not rooting well.

#33 - Their force is not round (flat).

#79 - The Chi not calm - heavy breathing.

#97 - Not balanced - it is easy to see.

#99 - Afraid.

These are the weak points. Do you have them? If so, pay more attention when you practice to improve. Otherwise you are easily defeated.

102) ... and once discovered attack without delay.

When you find out the weak points, your attack should go forward at once. (#26 - Judge the chance and take the opportunity to attack.) If the chance is lost, it will be hard to find another. Don't lose it. There is a story about taking the chance. They say the head of chance has some hair on its top, but it is bald in the back. When it comes to you, grab it by the hair - you can gain. If you lose the first opportunity, it is lost forever - you cannot grip a bald head.

103) The wrist, elbow, shoulder, hip and knee are all combined.

In line #68 it talks about the 5 terminals and the 9 joints. These are the 9 joints: 2 wrists, 2 elbows, 2 shoulders, 1 hip, 2 knees. All the nine joints should work together and conceal the inner force within them. They are controlled by the inner force. Practice slowly, evenly and calmly.

#91- There must be concentration of Spirit and Idea.

#92 - All the joints move together.

These two lines remind us that all joints continuously move as one. The internal force is concealed inside.

#93 - The inner force comes out at once. If you are relaxed, the inner force comes out whenever needed.

#94 - Opportunity - Be ready to send out at any time. The best way to do this is to hide (conceal) your inner force calmly.

104) Movement of legs and hands all work together.

Whenever you take a step, your hands should work with it. This means your hind leg pushes forward your body and hands without delay. Legs should be well rooted into the ground.

Working together is very important. The Mind's idea goes to the kidney for movement. Now, hands and legs move together without delay.

This is an example from business: When an idea comes into the manager's mind, he sends an order to all his assistants, salesmen, clerks, and messengers. If they all work together, it is a perfect company and should be successful in business. If part of the force doesn't work together, you can be sure the firm will fail. It is imperfect. Take time to practice daily, and get the order from the mind to the kidneys. We cannot do well to relax our muscles and joints in a short period. But you can get it within three months if you practice patiently, carefully and confidently.

105) All the joints work in combination with the Geng (Inner Force).

Geng is an important part of this internal exercise. It is concealed inside the joints. It can be developed with practice. When it is needed, it comes out without delay. It is unbelievable - like magic! If you don't study, you will have none; but if you practice daily for three months you can get it. You may like to play with it by stretching your fingers and make the Geng go forward to the tips. The more you practice, the more you gain.

For the main part, Geng comes mainly from the spine. The body must be balanced to allow the Geng to come out through the back of your body. The movements must be circular, the head up-raised, the abdomen relaxed. All attacks must be balanced, forward with backward, up and down, left with right.

All the muscles and joints work together with the Geng. Rooting must be firm.

106) If this is achieved, there is no chance for the enemy to attack.

The movements of all limbs are controlled by the kidney or spine. To speak clearly: Any movement we make from the kidney is expressed by the hands or the legs.

By practicing the combining of the whole body and by practicing this technique often, we give the enemy no chance to attack. We should pay attention to:

#1 - *Empty the mind. Softly smooth the movements. If there is no hindrance inside, you will arrive at the "natural state."*

#5 - *Harmony within and without. Meditation gives mental relaxation and help to the brain.*

#11 - Follow the Eight Methods:

1. Chi works internally concentrated by the Spirit.

2. Bone conceals the internal force.

3. Feature is fluid and continuous.

4. Follow the opponent's attack by yielding with circular motion.

5. Rise up the head, relaxed, as if suspended from above.

6. Return to and fro to maintain an even balance.

7. Restrain the mind to be calm.

8. Conceal the inner force until it is needed.

#14 - The entire body is elastic or spring-like -by circling big or small circles.

#18 - Relaxing and flexing of movement are self-determined by an imagined opponent in front of you.

#20 - The body should be straight in stance -face your attacker so you will not lose your balance.

#22 - Practice regularly to loosen your body without tightness.

#23 - Be rooted firmly by 'walking' and 'rowing' daily.

#48 - The body is both yin and yang, empty and solid, insubstantial and substantial.

#52 - Advancing and retreating use force derived from the kidney and spine.

#53 -Arms and back should be round as if hugging.

#54 - Circulate Chi from inside to outside.

#58 -Spirit watches in all directions.

#61 -Movement is like swimming or like stillness with an idea.

107) One's breathing is like the falling of fine cotton.

This is the work of the natural state. All gains and all growth are from the natural state. Breathing should be without any force in a calm, comfortable manner. That is why it is said that the breathing is like the falling of fine cotton. It is very gentle.

108) Therefore, your breathing can be up or down, slow or fast.

It is the natural way for the breathing to follow the principles of the natural state. Sometimes up, then down; sometimes fast, then slow. All the movements are circular and should be balanced. Take your breath as you need it.

109) When the method is mastered, any attack can be met.

When the method of movement is mastered well you can meet any attack; but until that time you had better stay away from fighting. We should not be too lazy or tired to practice daily. Our mind is made up to study by patience, meditation, slowness, calmness and circularity. It is especially important to concentrate on what we learn at first, for these are the basic movements. If they are mastered in the proper way it is easy to learn more and more. Many books advise that beginners learn little, but deeply. This is important. Do you move in the proper way? Watch your other schoolmates or your teacher and see <u>How</u> they move. Then you may copy the best movement you see.

In China, those who want to learn to write good characters meditate on a good Chinese character book. It gives a good impression to the mind of the learner. Then they write from their deep impression, and soon they can write very well. They make progress easily. We can do the same in learning this exercise. It will help to master the method.

This is only the first step.

As to the second step, you should understand the application of each movement: <u>Why</u> you should move in this way. As soon as you understand the <u>why</u> of each movement, you are moving in a proper way. For the third step, you must know the name of each movement. Then, as soon as your teacher or anyone calls out the name, you know what to do. But this is for beginners only.

When you learn deeper, you will understand that what you learn is Internal not External movement. An internal movement comes from the inside of your body - from the kidney or spine. All movements come from the inside and are expressed by the hands and legs on the outside.

Gradually the Chi and Geng (internal circulation and force) come out more and more. This makes your Chi and Geng control all outside movements. And your Idea and Spirit control your Chi and Geng. It goes step by step up, deeper and deeper. The more you practice, the more interest you will have.

110) Strive for knowledge of the method, but also the wisdom (craft) of its usage.

When we talk about meeting the attack by the method you learn, you should know how to make your method suitable. Wisdom changes the method into a suitable movement. This we call craft. Craft is shaped from wisdom and experience. The detail of truth is so fine that we have to meditate on its usage. A rough minded student cannot gain much, so we should carefully meditate on each movement bit by bit. The more you meditate, the more you gain. First we should master the method of movement; second, we should meditate the craft together with the movement to meet the enemy. Method and craft: the two must come together. This makes a wonderful art for fighting.

111) Method and wisdom are joined into one.

The method and wisdom to meet the enemy are two things, but at the same time make the two into one. This is lively cooperation; they work together and cannot be separated from each other. Use your wisdom to judge how to defeat your attacker with craft.

112) Both concepts are very important; there cannot be one without the other.

When you learn the method, use your wisdom and judgment to overcome your fierce attacker. Method and wisdom, like 2 hands and 2 legs working together, are very important in your fighting period. Don't waste your time and chance during such an emergency period. Method and wisdom together.

113) Both hands raise up lightly.

This refers to the beginning of the exercise when we raise both our hands lightly. Learning this movement before any other points out to the student the necessity of moving the hands lightly, slowly and evenly. The hands are round and move closer and closer, protectively, like a harbor. This movement is used to protect the head from a sudden two-fisted attack.

When the hands raise up lightly, people who are unfamiliar with internal work find it difficult to believe that such lightness of movement can be used for self-defense. But, training in softness, slowness and stillness, will make the arms as strong and as hard as a pair of steel bars. This is the wonderful aspect about Internal Kung Fu, although it takes a long time to master.

When you are doing the whole Form, this is the first movement you make. So, you have lightly raised up, lightly. It not say raise up quickly. So, lightly is smooth. Lightly the Chi will go up with your move and continuously and calmly. It will help your nerves. You have to take care of your balance -hand goes up and the Chi comes down or your hand comes down, the Chi goes up. That's balance. Therefore, also your head raise up, hand up, but the Chi goes down, the hand down, the body up.

Now, for application, if you meet the enemy he hits you to the side or holds your neck, your hand goes up, then to your eyebrow you turn and bring him into your body. When the two hands come down, raise up your head and raise up your knee and your knee goes to this bottom part. Very helpful. Beginners should always remember that the hands raise up lightly, <u>but not the shoulders</u>. Shoulders and elbows are low. This is the principle of the internal.

114) Bend and stretch fluidly.

Bending in angles is not fluidness. To stretch and to bend in circles is necessary for the circulation of the Chi to go to the tips of your fingers without getting stuck somewhere along the meridians within your body.

Stretching up straight is easy; however, to do so will not circulate your Chi. When you bend, lower your shoulder and elbow. Stretch out will help your Chi go to the tip of your fingers. Inside like steel. Your arm rounds like a harbor; like a bow. That's very important. If we're not round, you have no resistance. Round, therefore, bend and stretch. Bend and stretch. Stretch up and your weight comes down here. The hand up, the weight comes down. The idea comes down. The balance moves, too. The spine moves a little move. The spine's like an axle on your car. It moves slowly and your hands like a wheel. A little move in your spine and your hand moves a little. Therefore, the spine controls all your bow. If your spine not move, everything stops. You move a little bit, but go. When you're up, your Chi down. Your two legs not straight. Need to relax. Not bend too much - a little. Down your hand, up your leg. Your whole body has to move. We conceal; we don't show other people. So, bend and stretch. No anger. Smooth. That's important.

Line #33 explains: Conceal one's force like a bow, round and ready to spring.

Line #34: Attack as the arrow - quick and straight. This means that the inner force comes forth at once, because the arms and hands are rounded.

Line #52: Advancing and retreating use force derived from the spine. The inner force, quick and straight, is sent out first from your kidneys and spine. From this you can see that your spine is continuously moving. The spine turns slowly, calmly, and evenly. The spine's moving can determine simultaneous movement to all parts of the body. If you move only by one hand or leg, it is not right. A correct movement moves all together, controlled by the spine. All the above is bending and stretching fluidly.

115) All turning and bending is curved.

The turning and bending in hard Kung Fu is in straight lines, but in soft Kung Fu all the turning and bending is curved. The external martial arts meet attack with force - straight on, or bending at an angle. The internal meets attack with curves. Yielding to the force and guiding it to the empty is the way of the soft Kung Fu.

The external reveals its strength, while the internal conceals the force inside the bones and joints. Guide your attacker's strength into emptiness and then send out the internal force from the back of your attack. When the method of "yield" is mastered in pushing hands, a little turning and bending from the spine will guide the strength into the empty; then your opponent's balance is upset.

Train well to loosen and relax without hindrance. Then you can easily meet your enemy's attack. Practice your body movement well. The hand movements are all controlled by the body.

In China, Kung Fu is divided into two kinds: one is hard and one is soft. Hard is external. You can see it -- not concealed. But soft is concealed -- concealed in the curve. All round curve. All is circle -- round. If you meet attack, you do so by curve, like a snake. Curve not on the outside, but inside curved, too. Inside your body is a circle. The circle starts from your spine. Even when you shoot a gun, the bullet circles -- not straight. Therefore, the bullet comes through your body in a small circle, but it comes out a big hole because it circles out. So our movement also --same way.

116) The Form is like a swimming dragon in play.

The Form we practice can be viewed as a huge serpent swimming in the water: calmly up and down, left and right, changing the center of balance from left to right. It is like play, full of spirit and vitality. The whole Form so good to look. We can see when you practice up, sudden down; sudden left and sudden right. So beautiful, so graceful. It's fantastic and so freely, so lightly, so lively, so active, like a swimming dragon. The dragon's body submerges and surfaces, moving <u>like the heavy, surging waves of the sea</u>. These surges are deceptive in appearance, coming up smoothly and smoothly going down - but always with hidden force. Suddenly up and suddenly down in a playful manner.

That swimming serpent in play in water. That's nice to see, but if you don't do good, you must pay attention to your rooting. How about your footing? How about your walking? How about your rowing the boat? All basic Form you do very good. It's more important than you know the whole Form. If your footing's firm, then your whole body will relax. Nice to see. We never fall because rooting firmly and all our movements are combined in one; combined together. All movement is controlled by your spine and spine we do according to what wishes. Also raise up your head - you're more spiritual. Looks like a dragon - beautiful, spiritual, so active. Relax and underneath the foundation is firm, like a castle.

117) Therefore, all sides move up or down, left or right.

This sentence expresses the movement of the last line: The form is like a swimming dragon at play. At play, very relaxed, we can move in all directions. Up and down, left and right, forward, then backward, corner to corner; within your space you can have fluidness like a swimming dragon at play.

Your muscles and joints are trained to sense your attacker from all sides of your space without hindrance. With good training you will guide your attacker into empty and make him lose his balance. We must practice daily, all sides moving up and down like a swimming dragon at play.

118) This type of exercise follows the way of Yin and Yang. (Although never completely one or the other.)

Yin-Yang means opposite. What is Yin must Yang. Yin, they say, female. Yang is male. God makes the person in this world. He first makes Yang --says not good without company. *Makes him sleep in the Garden of Paradise and from his bone, takes out his bone to make a woman. When the man wakes up, he sees the woman come up to him and says this is bone of bone, flesh of flesh. So, he loves the woman so much -- his own bone, his own flesh. That's what the Bible says -- Yin-Yang. Other things in and out; it comes in and goes out. This Yin-Yang -- black and white --opposite. All is called Yin-Yang -- up and down, conceal-express -- Yin-Yang. Because of Yin-Yang, you have balance on all sides. When the right hand goes up, the left hand goes down--balance.*

Yin and yang are opposed to each other as are in and out, soft and hard, upper and lower. When we turn from yin and yang, we turn to pass the way from one part to the other; this is called "change." We turn this situation into the other situation. But remember that all changes originate in the Tan T'ien. The Tan T'ien is similar to a ball of compressed energy which rests in a dormant stage beneath the stomach, until its force is released through constant practice in T'ai Chi. Before the internal benefits of this exercise can be fully realized, the student must train well in order to release this stored energy.

In our exercise we know that gravity is rooted if our gravity is strong and balanced, all sides. Move natural, comfortable, all sides. Yin-Yang also comfortable. We enjoy our exercise; lightly relaxed and all your life to practice this exercise; comfortable, always happy with smiling, enjoy your health. Your body and soul should be happy, should be strong. You satisfy yourself, content yourself, smiling all the time.

119) The Idea is formed and the Chi follows.

The last two lines expressed the outer forms of the inside movement, but this sentence and the following one refer to the inner workings of movement.

As soon as an Idea is formulated in your mind, your Chi combines with the Idea. The Idea itself determines the move; the activation of Chi comes from training. Therefore, many people who train in T'ai Chi will stretch their fingers to ease the flow of Chi. Gradually the Chi will release its energy throughout the body.

Idea controls the Chi. When it goes up your hand, it is the Idea, and the Chi goes with the hand. Understand? So you do it slowly--don't quick.

All movements have a good idea. When you practice this exercise you must know the application, and the idea will follow your application; the Idea followed by Chi. You can do it everywhere and every minute. Whenever you move you have an Idea, and the Chi will go, too.

Geng, called inner force, comes up to meet any attack as a servant obeys a master. The Geng comes up from the bone. Two things inside: Chi follows the Idea and Geng they come up. Your thoughts express up. It comes up at once. Conceal-express. At any time people to attack you, natural you can meet your attacker and make him scared.

Train your mind to always protect yourself. Relax, and your mind and your brain, your physical, your hand, your leg, your body, your spine, everything sudden comes together to meet the attacker.

You have two faithful servants: Geng and Chi.

120) The Inner Force is concealed within the joints.

Inner Force is brought from the bone, then concealed within the joints. Therefore, the body must be kept round, with the hands and legs augmenting the body's roundness so the inner force can be issued through a circular path.

All joints conceal a kind of Geng inside. These things very valuable. Same as you keeping your money in a bank. You have your Chi inside your bone. Your bone is your bank. When you need , it comes up. You train it, you save it. It is so valuable that when it comes up it is like steel--very hard. You have such a kind of Geng inside. They can protect fierce foe against you. That's a very valuable thing.

Line #34 mentions "Attack as an arrow - quick and straight" because the inner force can come out clearly from a circular path. From line #33: "Conceal one's force like a bow, round and ready to spring," we can see that all the body movements should be bow-like. Observe the following:

> #51 -The legs should be curved like a bow.

> #53 -The arms and back should be round as if hugging.

> #54 - Circulate your Chi from inside to outside. Only round circulates well.

> #93 - When contact is made, the inner force comes forth at once.

> #94 -This gives no opportunity for the opponent to escape.
> From loose muscles where inner force is concealed, there is
> swift and quick attack.

> #97 -All movement is balanced in a circular fashion. Remember,
> not only quick, but balanced.

> #105 - All the joints work in combination with the inner force. In this
> manner, at any time the inner force should be ready to utilize.

> #116 - The form is like a swimming dragon at play. The Idea, Chi and
> inner force work in combination so that your form is beautiful like a
> swimming dragon at play.

121) Relax your muscles and activate your blood vessels.

Muscles are relaxed by slow movements. Loose muscles enable your Chi and circulation to go through all parts of your body, even to the tips of your fingers. This is not only good for your health, but also good for making your movements fast without hindrance.

"Slow makes fast" is the principle of this internal exercise. Therefore, a fluid movement will relax the muscles and activate the blood vessels. Whoever requires health and strength should practice this exercise daily with slowness, evenness, and calmness; always with curved movements in all parts of your body, hands and legs. (And remember, all movements are linked together without stopping or jerking.)

Gradually you will gain a ball of Chi under your stomach which will get stronger and stronger. Hard as a rock, but soft as it is easily moved. This Tan T'ien can be gained only by frequent practice, and when you gain it you are in an advanced stage. You can utilize the Tan T'ien to control the movement of all parts of the body. The arms and legs and even the torso are controlled to move by the Tan T'ien. When your hands and arms are as strong as iron bars and your touch is directed by the Tan T'ien, your touch will cause the opponent to fall. This force comes out of the whole body, which is heavy and strong.

The Tan T'ien is directed by the Idea of the Mind. Whenever your Idea wishes to do, your Chi will come out at once from the Tan T'ien. To the right or left, up or down, all sides as you wish; like a swimming dragon at play.

This martial art is a wonderful thing--a valuable thing. It's a wonderful exercise. You get Chi and Geng by these slow movements.

122) This is good for one's health.

This exercise is good for your health as well as your self-defense. Relaxed kidneys and loosened arms and legs will give you a swift attack to your opponent far better than hard boxing can do, because relaxing is the best self-defense.

Relaxation will give you a good appetite. The slow movements up and down and left and right and all around will grind and grind at all the undigested food and out of your stomach; then you will feel hungry and want to eat and drink.

Exercise will make you tired and you will want a good sleep. Meditate on your movement, stop thinking of the other things and you will give your brain to rest and conserve your energy for your daily work. This is good for one's health.

The benefit of learning T'ai Chi: diseases can be prevented, illness inside can be pushed out, the weak can be strong. Many proofs can be testified by those who practice exercise. This is a good exercise for gentlemen and ladies, young and old, female and male. When you make up your mind to learn, after one year you will prove my work.

123/124) When inhaling, the Chi rises. When exhaling, the Chi sinks to the Tan T'ien.

These two lines talk about breathing when the exercise is mastered. Beginners should take breath in naturally at first. When you gain a Tan T'ien under your stomach, you can make use of it to breathe and move. The Tan T'ien is also called the Sea of Chi. When inhaling your Chi rises. When exhaling your Chi goes back to the Tan T'ien or say, the Chi goes back to the Sea. This should be done in a natural way. The Tan T'ien is the right instrument for you to practice linking breathing and movement together. But this is for the advanced state.

125) As soon as the Chi rises, it is swallowed and sinks down.

When you raise up your Chi, it is natural that you sink your Chi by swallowing. The Chi rises up the back and sinks down to the abdomen by swallowing. It sinks down to the Sea of Chi, or Tan T'ien. By means of the Tan T'ien, you can move more with Chi. It is an important part of the advanced study. It can only be gained by practice every day. You will also gain relaxation in all your muscles, strengthened muscles, Geng *concealed in the bones and the joints, the ball of Chi under your stomach and the Chi will flow throughout your body. You will be surprised to gain better health: good appetite, increased energy, more patience than before, mental work resumed and internal illness abolished.*

The movements rise and sink with the Chi. It is interesting like a swimming dragon in play.

126) (In the flow of Chi) fire from below and water from above meet harmoniously.

When the water comes up and the fire sinks down it is a harmonious state. If no strength is used, if your inner force is concealed inside the bones and joints, your temper will be calm and cool. They say that the water comes up.

If one uses hard strength to practice, if the chest is thrown out, the eye is red and the temper is hot, they say the fire comes up. The temper grows bad easily.

When water and fire work together harmoniously there is great energy, like a steaming kettle. All forces are in balance and everything seems to be in order. But you must take care of this balance. If the water boils over, the fire will be extinguished. If the fire gets too hot, the water will evaporate.

The external exercise came first, but as the advanced work came up, it slowly changed to the internal work which is good for the health, too. Improvement was made from generation to generation. After 45 years, it no longer benefits to study the hard Kung Fu, but the internal you can practice all your life, even if have 100 years of age. There are many people who practice this exercise in Hong Kong and Red China because they want to enjoy a better health. In this troubled world, we use a lot of energy to make our daily living. It gives us too much fire and spoils our health and tempo. But if we learn this internal exercise we can make harmony and enjoy our lives peacefully.

127) Carefully study this inside and outside Kung Fu.

This sentence gives an idea to the advanced who has been training in the Kung Fu to the highest point. They should not stop and think that it is enough. They should carefully study this inside as well as Kung Fu. Then you will be perfect in the martial arts. If you are well trained in both, you can easily meet all kinds of people in all parts of the world without fear.

128) The mind (heart) should be empty; the abdomen should be solid.

A well-trained student should be empty in the mind and solid in the abdomen. The abdomen is the lower part of the body, and the mind is the upper part of the body. If the lower part is heavy and the upper part is light you can stand firmly like a mountain. This exercise is derived from the I-Ching: the upper part of a given hexagon being heaven and the lower part being earth, with man in the middle. It is natural then that heaven is light and earth is heavy. We should make ourselves firm and steady, balanced between heaven and earth. This principle does not change with internal or external Kung Fu. Remember, the mind (heart) is empty and the abdomen is solid. This idea is referred to in line #124: The Chi sinks to the *Tan T'ien*.

129) At the moment of opportunity, attack at once.

Opportunity is hard to get. It comes, then remains for only a little time and goes away as quickly as it came. Therefore, we should seize the chance to act when opportunity is at hand. Whenever you find that your enemy is slack, such as when there is an opening of his hands, attack him at once, in his weakness. This is how to profit from your sudden advance.

130) The beginning and end of hardness and softness are inseparable.

Your sudden advancing is mostly hardness, but with softness you can change the circumstances into a profitable condition. The beginning circles into the end, and the end circles into the beginning. This is yin and yang. The art of moving is to be different and changeable at all times. Yin and yang, hardness and softness, fist and palms. For self-defense, hardness and softness are inseparable; all comes together.

131) The outside and inside force are mutually interchangeable.

We can attack from outside as well as inside, which is also yin and yang. Yin and Yang means changeable. Suddenly attack the outside and suddenly attack the inside. We can use both. A well-trained student can do this without problem. A well-trained student can

meet the attack on the outside, turn the attack away, and then return the attack from the inside. (This is like Push the Boat.) But this is not for the beginners. The beginners have to practice frequently -- whenever you find time to practice during the day. Practice makes perfect. When you are in perfect, you find it easy to use your force according to your wishes.

132) Activity and inactivity follow one's will.

Inactivity and activity are yin and yang. All things opposite to each other are yin and yang as we have just learned: softness and hardness, palms and fists, inside and outside, calm and moving, slow and quick. All such yin and yang meet in what you wish to do. Activity and inactivity follow one's will. For self-defense, we yield to our attacker with softness, then follow soft with hard and, with a little force, a little touch applied to his oncoming force, he is sure to lose his balance. The heavier the attack that is coming to me, the heavier my opponent's fall will be. When I yield to heavy advance (by swift movements from my relaxed muscles), his attack will follow towards my emptiness, and he will fall.

Relaxation of the muscles is an important lesson for the beginner. That is the secret of this exercise. As a merchant should have capital for business, we should have relaxation for self-defense.

133/134) Those who set out to learn the exercise, do not misjudge the value of The Chinese Five Word Song.

Those who make up their mind to learn the exercise, do not misjudge the value of this Five Word Song which is the principle of Hwa Yu T'ai Chi Ch'uan Kung Fu. It has been a great help to thousands of students for over a thousand years. The value of the Song's principles have been proven from generation to generation. That it can maintain so long in history and prove its value, it is worthwhile to honor it and study it and meditate on these principles because it will benefit your health and self-defense.

Appendix

We are most fortunate that Grand Master John Chung Li passed along a wealth of information to Master Xavier, including many documents and pictures.

We begin by sharing The Chinese Five Word Song and Six Combinations, Eight Methods with Master Li's drawings of Chinese characters.

Next, we share a picture of Master Li from his days in Hong Kong followed by pictures of Masters Li and Xavier from Boston in the 1970's and a more recent picture of Master Xavier. This copy of The Chinese Five Word Song becomes a marvelous insight into Internal Boxing as well as the history of Master Li's knowledge and wisdom into life.

We invite you to learn more about Hwa-Yu T'ai-Chi Ch'uan by visiting the official web site at www.gmaf.org/hwa-yu.html. You will find information about the history, principles and practice of Hwa-Yu T'ai-Chi along with details about ordering instructional video tapes featuring Master Xavier and his senior students. We welcome your questions and comments about Hwa-Yu T'ai-Chi Ch'uan and The Chinese Five Word Song. You can e-mail mmcgee@gmaf.org or write to Hwa-Yu T'ai-Chi, P.O. Box 360383, Tampa, FL 33673-0383.

Thank you for your interest in this ancient martial art and healthcare science. We hope it blesses you the way it has us.

Mark McGee
January 2004

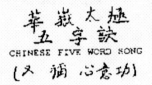

華嶽太極
五字訣
CHINESE FIVE WORD SONG
（又 稱 心意功）

心 意 本 無 法

1. Empty the mind.

有 法 是 虛 無

2. If one thinks there is a method, that thought is in vain.

虛 無 得 自 然

3. By making the mind void of thoughts, one can gain a
   natural meditative state.

無 法 不 容 恕

4. With a calm mind, one is free from hesitation.

放 之 弥 六 合

5. A quiet mind opens the pathway to harmony within and
   without.

包 羅 小 天 地

6. Fill the sky and the earth within as well as without.

繹 家 為 圓 覺

7. This is like the Buddhist's idea conveyed by the circle.

道 家 說 無 為

8. The Taoists say it is not one's will, but the will of nature.

有 象 求 無 象

9. At first while doing the exercise, one reveals each feature of the
   movement, but with practice the features flow into one.

83

不 期 自 然 至

10. This fluidness of movement cannot be anticipated; through practice it comes naturally.

要 學 心 意 功　　　*12* 先 從 八 法 起

11. If one wishes to learn this internal exercise, the one must first learn the eight methods. (Internal Kung Fu)

養 我 浩 然 氣

13. This exercise maintains one's broadminded spirit.

遍 身 皆 彈 力

14. The entire body is elastic (spring-like).

見 首 不 見 尾

15. The beginning of the internal force can be recognized by the opponent, but not its end.

無 象 亦 無 意

16. When the exercise is mastered, one's feature and intent are unrecognizable.

收 放 勿 露 形

17. Movement to and fro is not revealed.

鬆 緊 要 自 主

18. Relaxing and flexing of movement are self-determined.

禦 應 宜 守 默

19. One must meet attack by being calm.

不 偏 亦 不 倚

20. The body should be straight in stance.

視不能而能

21. The opponent sees no resistance in your stance, but this is false for you are concealed.

生疏莫臨敵

22. If one does not practice regularly, then do not face the enemy.

動時把得固

23. When in motion one is still rooted.

一發未深入

24. Do not overextend yourself to the opponent.

審機得其勢

25. Judge the chance and take the opportunity.

乘勞喜弓顧

26. One strikes with internal force before the opponent advances with strength.

剛在他力前

27. When the opponent is hard, then one is soft.

柔乘他力後　29彼忙我靜待

28. Although the opponent is busy, one stays clam awaiting him.

後守任君鬥

30. To attack or protect is according to one's decision.

步步占先機

31. Take the first opportunity and be quicker than the opponent.

時時要留意

32. Always concentrate on the situation.

蓄力如弓圓

33. Conceal one's force like the bow, round and ready to spring.

發勁似箭直

34. Attack as the arrow- quick and straight.

悟透陰陽理

35. One should thoroughly understand the principle of yin-yang.

剛柔互參就

36. Both the yin and yang flow in and out, hard and soft, and are of mutual use.

調息坎離交

37. Breathing is regular from the bottom of the abdomen to the heart.

上下中和氣

38. This cyclic up and down breathing smoothes the chi.

守默如卧禪

39. Be calm as the resting Buddhists.

勁似蟄龍起

40. Move as a dragon rising from hibernation.

虛灵含有物

41. This calmness appears empty but there is something within.

窈窈冥冥趣

42. The internal force is wonderfully rewarding.

忽隱又忽現

43. The internal force can be suddenly concealed and suddenly expressed.

息息任自然

44. All breathing shall be natural.

避免敵重力

45. Yield to heavy attack.

原來自我始

46. Every action is self initiated.

双 单 可 分 明

47. Distribution of weight between one leg and the other is clearly distinguished.

陰 陽 見 虚 实

48. The body is of both yin and yang, both empty and solid.

虚 引 敵 落 空

49. By emptying oneself, the opponent's force is lead to a void.

欲 收 放 变 急

50. If the enemy retreats, stick with quick advance.

兩 腿 似 弓 彎

51. The legs should be curved like a bow.

伸 缩 膁 着 力

52. Advancing and retreating use force derived from the kidney.

臂 脊 須 圓 抱

53. The arms and back should be round as if hugging.

內 外 混 元 氣

54. Circulate your chi from inside to outside.

意 念 要 集 神 56 彷 彿 臨 大 敵

55. Stop trivial thoughts and concentrate on your movement, as if facing a difficult enemy.

目 光 如 流 電

57. Your eyes move about like lightening.

錯 神 顧 四 陽

58. Your spirit watches in all four directions (front, back, left, right).

前 四 後 似 六

59. Your footing should be 40% to the front and 60% to the rear.

拿 擺 三 分 七

60. The hands are 30% to the front and 70% to the rear.

若 履 雲 霧 霧   63. 飘 飘 乎 欲 仙

61. The feature of the movement is like swimming in the water.

形 動 如 洛 水

62. Movement is light like a fairy in the clouds.

浩 浩 乎 清 虛

64. The idea is very great, but there is nothing; it is like a great void.

意 動 似 懼 虎

65. The idea of movement is like a fierce tiger.

氣 靜 如 處 子

66. The calmness of chi is very gentle.

犯 者 敢 即 仆

67. Once the enemy is offensive, the enemy is defeated.

五 總 九 節 力

68. The inner strength controls the five terminals and the nine joints.

欲 學 持 有 恒

69. If one wants to learn, then one must practice frequently.

升 堂 可 入 室

70. In this way deeper progress can be made. (From the door to hall, to temple with one's master.)

顯 隱 無 不 有

71. When the exercise is mastered, one's inner force can be concealed or expressed at will.

72. Focus your spirit to discover the truth.

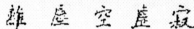

73. This harmonious exercise combines all movement.

凝 歷 空 虛 寂

74. The quiet and emptiness of this exercise separates one from worldly things.

75. Remember all progress towards the truth of this exercise is very delicate.

欲 動 似 非 動

77. The idea of movement is to seem not to move, achieving fluidness.

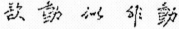

78. One's calmness combines with the idea

急 念 氣 自 平

79. Cease all thoughts and your *chi* will become calm naturally.

默 默 守 太 虛

80. Quietly maintain the "great emptiness".

元 根 筑 基 法

81. One's basic foundation is built through this exercise.

蘊 藏 皆 珠 玉

82. In this exercise all valuable points are concealed.

說 難 亦 非 難

83. If you ask, "Is it hard to learn?", the answer is "No it is not."

看 易 本 非 易

84. It looks easy at first, but it is not easy.

有 志 事 竟 成

85. If one's mind is made up to learn, then there will be success.

世 间 無 難 事

86. In this world there is nothing of real difficulty.

敬 學 累 有 試

87. To learn, one must be sincere and determined.

久 恒 与 智 慧

88. This depends on long frequent practice and wisdom.

華 嶽 希 夷 門

89. This exercise was invented by Ch'en His I of Hwa Yü.

力 行 最 為 貴

90. The student of Hwa Yu should practice every day; this is most important.

神 意 要 集 中

91. There must be concentration of spirit and idea(will).

推 動 輪 轉 器

92. All the joints of the body move together.

一 觸 力 即 發

93. When contact is made, the inner force comes forth at once.

推 動 輪 轉 器

94. This gives no opportunity for the opponent to escape.

敵 鬆 似 非 鬆

95. The opponent thinks your are relaxed, but you are not relaxed (inner strength).

欺緊求着力
96. The opponent thinks you are tight, but there is no strength.

逗使來均衡
97. All the movement is balanced in a circular fashion.

螺旋循讓氣
98. The chi should be controlled to flow in and out in a spiraling circle.

進敵莫惧路
99. Do not be afraid of the opponent.

開固收与放
100. Open and close oneself and be able to yield and stick.

見形尋破綻  102絲毫不相讓
101. Watch for the enemy's weak point, and once discovered, attack without delay.

腕肘肩胯膝
103. The wrist, elbow, shoulder, hip and knee are all combined.

足踏手脚齊
104. Movement of legs and hands all work together.

節節力貫亭
105. All the joints work in combination with the geng (inner force).

處處無罅隙
106. If this is achieved, there is no chance for the enemy to attack.

呼吸細綿綿
107. One's breathing is like the falling of fine cotton.

升降緩而急
108. Therefore, your breathing can be up or down, slow or fast.

得法可应变
109. When this method is mastered, any attack can be met.

有術方為奇
110. Strive for knowledge of the method, but also the wisdom (craft) of
its usage.

法術二而一
111. Method and wisdom are joined into one.

缺一不能互
112. Both concepts are very important; there cannot be one without the
other.

兩手輕輕起
113. Both hands raise up lightly.

曲伸無斷續
114. Bend and stretch fluidly.

尊移有曲折
115. All turning and bending is curved.

形似游龍戲
116. The form is like a swimming dragon in play.

縱橫與起伏
117. Therefore, all sides move up or down, left or right.

陰陽運行教
118. This type of exercise follows the way of yin and yang.

意動氣相隨
119. The idea is formed and the chi follows.

關節含蓄力
120. The inner force is concealed within the joints.

舒筋活血脈
121. Relax your muscles and activate your blood vessels.

榮衛得適宜
122. This is good for one's health.

92

一 吸 氣 便 起

123. When inhaling, the chi rises.

氣 氣 可 歸 臍

124. When exhaling, the chi sinks to the tan tien.

一 起 氣 便 咽

125. As soon as the chi rises, it is swallowed and sinks down.

水 火 得 相 見

126. (In the flow of chi) fire from below and water from above meet harmoniously.

精 研 內 外 功

127. Carefully study this inside and outside Kung-fu

心 虛 腹 宜 實

128. The mind (heart) should be empty; the abdomen should be solid.

率 然 取 其 勢

129. At the moment of opportunity, attack at once.

首 尾 不 相 離

130. The beginning and end of hardness and softness are inseparable.

奇 正 得 相 生

131. The outside and inside force are mutually interchangeable.

動 靜 隨 心 歌

132. Activity and inactivity follow one's will.

蠡 或 五 字 誤　　134 後 學 莫 輕 視

133. Those who set out to learn the exercise, do not misjudge the value of the five word song.

SIX COMBINATIONS AND EIGHT METHODS

SIX COMBINATIONS 六合

1. The body combines with the mind
2. The mind combines with the idea
3. The idea combines with the chi
4. The chi combines with the spirit
5. The spirit combines with the movement
6. The movement combines with the air

體合於心
心合於意
意合於氣
氣合於神
神合於動
動合於空

EIGHT METHODS 八法

1. Chi - The Chi works internally, concentrated by one's spirit.

氣：充氣集神

2. Bone - The internal force is concealed.

骨：骨勁內斂

3. Feature - Movement is fluid and continuous.

形：化身模仿

4. Follow - Meet an attack with circular movement, interpreting the force and yielding to it.

隨：圍隨篡奪

5. Rise - One's head is held as if suspended from above and relaxed.

提：項懸虛空

6. Return - To maintain an even balance, movement in one direction is tied to its opposite (to and fro, up and down, left and right)

還：往來返復

7. Restrain - The mind should be calm, maintaining an inner void.

靜：靜定守虛

8. Conceal - The inner force is concealed until it is needed.

伏：應接藏機

Grand Master John Chung Li (Hong Kong 1960)

Masters John Li and Robert Xavier (1975)

Masters John Chung Li and Robert Xavier (1976)

Master Robert Xavier (1999)

Lineage Holder / Chief Instructor

Hwa-Yu T'ai-Chi Ch'uan
Yon Ch'uan Martial Arts